LISTEN WITH MOTHER STORIES

In 1950, when Listen with Mother became radio's first programme for children under five, no research had been made into young children listening to stories. The child under five usually insists that a tale be told in the same way every time, so we could not use well known traditional tales. But a child unfamiliar with the stories would not understand without the pictures to help along the meaning. So we had to find a new literature. We found that if we put the choice in the children's hands by observing them well, sensing their needs and preferences, we made few mistakes. The subjects are endless, springing from their environment, from a memory of some rare pleasure they wish to share and relive, or from something quite new which must be made familiar before it can become part of the background of experience. People often ask "what about fairies?" I feel that for this age it is only necessary to have a few stories of the 'unseen playmate' variety rather than those that deal with the hierarchy of fairyland. If wisely used, the young child's fantasy is not an escape from reality, but one way of gradually coming to grips with it.

Storytelling should be a shared experience. It is an everyday event going on all over the world between adults and children. All that is needed is a readiness to enter simply and wholeheartedly into the storymaking game. But the first rate writer usually turns out to be a professional. That's not surprising, for story writing has its practising experts like any other craft.

It gives me great pleasure to introduce this wise selection of Listen with Mother stories made by Dorothy Edwards. Her Naughty Little Sister tales were one of our great finds in the early days of the programme. Those and many she has written since, illustrate aptly the qualities which make a story memorable instead of a merely transient experience. If the selection is controlled by a true appraisal of the child's needs and interests, the story hour may be a time of inestimable value to reader and listener, a time which links the present with the past and future, a time which can provide another field in which intellectual and imaginative development can take place quite naturally.

JEAN SUTCLIFFE

Also available in Young Lions

Jenny and the Cat Club *Esther Averill*
Simon and the Witch *Margaret Stuart Barry*
The Return of the Witch *Margaret Stuart Barry*
A Bear Called Paddington *Michael Bond*
The Reluctant Dragon *Kenneth Grahame*
The House That Sailed Away *Pat Hutchins*
Follow That Bus! *Pat Hutchins*
The Gingerbread Rabbit *Randall Jarrell*
The Demon Bike Rider *Robert Leeson*
Challenge in the Dark *Robert Leeson*
A Children's Zoo *Julia Watson (ed.)*
Rabbiting On *Kit Wright*
The Boy Who Sprouted Antlers *John Yeoman & Quentin Blake*

Listen with Mother Stories

Chosen by
DOROTHY EDWARDS

illustrated by Caroline Sharpe

Young Lions

All the stories in this collection were first broadcast in the Listen with Mother *programme. Some were subsequently published in book form. We are grateful to those publishers who have given us permission to reproduce copyright material, and where there are printed sources these are acknowledged at the end of the story.*

First published in Great Britain 1972
by the British Broadcasting Corporation
First published in Young Lions 1979
Fifth impression April 1989

Young Lions is an imprint of
the Children's Division, part of
the Collins Publishing Group,
8 Grafton Street, London W1X 3LA

Printed and bound in Great Britain by
William Collins Sons & Co. Ltd, Glasgow

Contents

The Black Kitten

Jean Sutcliffe

Once upon a time there was a little black kitten.

He had no mother.

He had no father.

He had no home at all.

So he wanted someone to look after him and feed him and give him a nice place to sleep in.

He set off down the road to find someone who would give him all those things.

He came to a baker's shop and stepped inside.

How warm it was! What nice smells.

How quiet it was. What a lot of bread, and buns, and cakes – all ready to sell. But nothing for a kitten to eat.

The black kitten said, "Miaow." But nobody heard. So he said it louder, and twice: "Miaow, miaow."

Still nobody heard.

Then he jumped up onto the counter right in front of the shop-lady and said "Miaow," again.

"What a dear little kitten," said the shop-lady. "Where did you spring from?" And she stroked him gently and smiled.

And the kitten arched his back and held his tail high up in the air and turned his head and smiled too – and purred.

"There now, Pussy," said the shop-lady. "That's enough. Jump down and let me get on with my work."

And she picked him up gently and put him down on the floor and said: "Shoo, shoo, off you go home, off you go home."

But of course the kitten had no home to go to, had he?

So he walked out of the baker's shop because no one wanted to look after him there. Next he came to a fish-shop, and stepped inside. How chilly it was! How damp the floor seemed. But what a delicious smell! Fish – all sorts of fish. A kitten could eat *everything* in this shop.

The black kitten said, "Miaow." But nobody heard. Then he said it again, louder and twice: "Miaow, miaow."

And at once a huge ginger cat came round the corner and looked down at him and said, "What do you want?"

"Someone to look after me," said the black kitten.

"I am cat to this fish-shop," said the ginger cat. "Go before I chase you out."

So the black kitten turned round and went out of the fish-shop quickly.

By this time he was feeling tired. And hungry. And thirsty. So he looked round about him, wondering where next he should go.

Then he saw two little girls called Mary and Alice coming along. Mary was carrying a baby doll and Alice was wheeling an empty dolls' pram.

Alice said: "Put her in the pram now, Mary, you've carried her long enough."

But Mary said: "No, she's my doll, and I'll carry her as long as I like."

"Then I'll put that kitten in the pram, and pretend he's my baby," said Alice.

And before the kitten had time to think, she picked him up and put him in the pram!

"There, Pussy," said Alice, "now you be good and pretend to be my little boy. I'll call you Peter. Lie down." And the kitten did lie down, for the pram was nice and soft. And Alice put a cover over him so that he felt warm. This was good. He had a name now: Peter. Everyone would call him Peter. Peter yawned and smiled and closed his blue eyes, and started to purr.

"Ah, Peter's going to sleep," said Alice. "Look, just like a baby." And she started to wheel the pram slowly along the pavement singing *Bye Baby Bunting*.

"Are you really going to take Peter home and have him for your little boy?" whispered Mary.

"Yes," said Alice, and went on singing *Bye Baby Bunting*.

"What if he belongs to someone else?" said Mary.

"He doesn't," said Alice.

"But what if he *does?*" said Mary.

"Then I'll ask them to let him stay with me always, and they will," said Alice, and she went on singing.

Well, by this time they were at home and Alice said: "I'm going to get Peter's milk, he always has it as soon as he wakes up." For by this time Alice felt as if he'd always been her own little boy.

And when Peter woke up she lifted him out of the pram and said: "Did you have a nice sleep, dear? Now, drink up your milk." And there was a saucer of warm, white milk!

Peter drank and drank and drank and drank until he looked as fat as a little barrel.

Then Alice said: "Finished, dear? That's a good boy; now you must go to bed." And she put him into a dolls' bed and covered him up all snug and warm.

Peter yawned. This was good. Here was somebody who wanted to look after him. She would feed him. *And* give him a nice place to sleep in.

He'd found a home, and a good one too!

The first story broadcast in the *Listen with Mother* programme.

Published in *Jacko and Other Stories* (Bodley Head).

Sarah Jane's Surprise

Elizabeth Robinson

Sarah Jane was in bed, beginning to get better from measles, and she was feeling very sorry for herself. She had played all her games and looked at all of her books, and now she didn't know what to do. Sarah Jane's mother was tidying her bed, when the telephone rang.

"I wonder who that can be?" said Sarah Jane.

"I had better go and see," said her mother.

When she came back, Sarah Jane's mother said, "That was Granny-by-the-sea. She says she hopes you are feeling much better now, and would you like to go and stay with her."

"Oh, yes please," said Sarah Jane, bouncing up and down on her bed with excitement. "When can I go, Mummy?"

"Well," said her mother, "the doctor said that you can go out on Saturday, that is in five days' time. So you can go on Saturday afternoon. The sea air will do you good."

"I can't wait until Saturday," said Sarah Jane, sighing.

"Oh, yes you can," laughed her mother. "There is something else that I have to tell you from Granny. She has a surprise for you when you visit her."

"I wonder what it can be?" said Sarah Jane.

"I don't know what it is, but it is something or someone to keep you company. You have four days to guess what it is. Granny says she will telephone every evening for the next four days to see how you are, and you can have one guess each evening."

"And on the fifth day I can go and stay with Granny-by-the-sea," said Sarah Jane happily, snuggling down in bed.

"Yes," said her mother. "And now you must go to sleep. Goodnight, dear, sleep well."

Sarah Jane thought that she would never be able to sleep with so many exciting things to think about, but she did.

The next day Sarah Jane thought and thought, and by teatime she had made up her mind what her first guess would be.

"I think it will be a puppy – my surprise, I mean," she said to her mother. "A black-and-white puppy, and I shall call him Spot. He will be able to play on the beach with me. I do hope it is a puppy."

But when Sarah Jane's granny telephoned that evening, she said the surprise wasn't a black-and-white puppy.

Sarah Jane was rather disappointed at first, but she soon cheered up and started to think what her next guess would be.

The next evening she said to her mother, "I have thought and thought, and I think Granny's surprise is a kitten, a tabby kitten. I shall call him Sam. Sam won't be able to play on the beach with me, but he will curl up on my knee in the evenings."

"That would be very nice," said her mother.

But when Sarah Jane's granny telephoned that evening she said no, the surprise wasn't a kitten. Sarah Jane would have to guess again.

"Oh – I did want it to be a kitten," said Sarah Jane, sadly.

"Never mind," said her mother, "now you can guess again. You have only two more guesses and two more days, and then off you go to stay with Granny-by-the-sea."

The next day when Sarah Jane's mother brought her tea-tray in she said: "What shall I tell Granny-by-the-sea tonight?"

"I have decided that my surprise will be a budgie," said Sarah Jane. "It will be a blue budgie in a cage and I shall call him Sparkly. He won't be able to play on the beach with me or curl up on my knee, but I shall be able to teach him to talk."

But when Sarah Jane's granny telephoned that night she said that the surprise wasn't a budgie.

"WHATEVER can it be?" said Sarah Jane. She thought harder than ever before the next day, because it was her last guess. When it was almost time for her granny to telephone she said to her mother: "I think that Granny's surprise MUST be a hamster. He will eat nuts from my hand and I shall buy a wheel to go in his cage so that he can ride round and round. But I can't think of a name for him."

Sarah Jane's mother thought, and Sarah Jane thought, but they couldn't think of a name for a hamster. While they were still thinking the telephone rang.

"That will be Granny-by-the-sea," said Sarah Jane excitedly. "Perhaps she will be able to think of a name. Hurry, Mummy!"

Sarah Jane's mother smiled. "I think you are well enough to speak to Granny-by-the-sea yourself tonight," she said.

Sarah Jane hurried to the telephone. "Sarah Jane Gray speaking," she said.

"Hello, Sarah Jane Gray," said Granny in a smiling voice. "Granny-by-the-sea here. Have you guessed my surprise yet?"

"I think it must be a hamster," said Sarah Jane. "Is it a hamster, Granny-by-the-sea?"

"No, it isn't a hamster. Just hang on a minute, Sarah Jane." Then Sarah Jane heard a voice she did not know. "Hello, Sarah Jane," said the voice, "I am your cousin Caroline. I have had measles, too, and I am staying with Granny-by-the-sea too. I am your surprise!"

"What a lovely, lovely surprise!" said Sarah Jane. A real little girl to play with. That was even better than a puppy or a kitten, or a budgie or a hamster.

"Goodbye, Sarah Jane," said Caroline. "Granny wants to talk now. See you tomorrow."

"Goodbye, Caroline," said Sarah Jane. "I will bring my new doll and all her clothes."

"Well, Sarah Jane," said her granny's voice. "How do you like my surprise?"

"I think it is the loveliest surprise of all," said Sarah Jane. "Thank you very, very much. Now Mummy wants to talk."

And while her mother was talking, Sarah Jane got busy packing her best doll's clothes in a tiny suitcase, ready to go to her Granny's-by-the-sea.

Singing in the Sunshine

Lily Bottomley

There was once a little donkey in a field, and nearby a blackbird was perched on the fence, singing gaily.

"That's a nice noise you're making, blackbird," said the little donkey. "What are you doing?"

"I'm singing," said the blackbird. "Tweet tweet."

"What for?" asked the donkey.

"I'm singing because the sun is shining," said the blackbird. "Tweet tweet."

"Oh, I'll sing too," said the donkey. "Hee-haw, hee-haw, hee-haw!"

A cow looked over the hedge to see what was happening. "What are you doing?" asked the cow.

"We're singing because the sun is shining," said the donkey. "Hee-haw, hee-haw."

"Oh, I'll sing too," said the cow. "Moo, moo, moo."

A little lamb came galloping along to see. "What are you doing?" asked the lamb.

"We're singing because the sun is shining," said the cow. "Moo, moo."

"Oh, I'll sing too," said the lamb. "Baa, baa, baa."

Then the farm dog came dashing along. "What's all the noise about?" asked the dog.

"We're singing because the sun is shining," said the lamb. "Baa, baa."

"Oh, I'll sing too," said the dog. "Bow-wow, bow-wow."

The farm cat had been sleeping on the window-sill. It woke up and bounced along to see what was going on. "What are you doing?" asked the cat.

"We're singing because the sun is shining," said the dog. "Bow-wow, bow-wow."

"Oh, I'll sing too," said the cat. "Miaow, miaow, miaow."

There was a duck swimming on the pond close by. It flew out of the water and waddled up. "Whatever are you doing?" asked the duck.

"We're singing because the sun is shining," said the pussycat. "Miaow, miaow."

"Oh, I'll sing too," said the duck. "Quack, quack, quack."

So they all kept on singing because the sun was shining.

"Quack, quack," sang the duck.

"Miaow, miaow," sang the cat.

"Bow-wow," sang the dog.

"Baa, baa," sang the lamb.

"Moo, moo," sang the cow.

"Tweet, tweet," sang the blackbird.

But the donkey sang loudest of all. "Hee-haw, hee-haw, hee-haw!"

All because the sun was shining!

Donkey Wants to Swim

Lily Bottomley

One morning the little donkey was having a walk in the field, and he came to the pond where the ducks were swimming.

"Hee-haw! What are you doing in the pond?" he asked.

"Quack, quack! We're swimming," said the ducks.

"*I* want to be a duck and swim too," said the little donkey. "How do you do it, hee-haw?"

"Quack, quack! Come down into the water," said the ducks, "and sit and move your legs about."

So the little donkey paddled out into the water and tried to sit on it, like the ducks. But he was much too heavy, and he sank to the bottom. He came up splashing and spluttering.

"Oh!" he shouted. "I can't do it! Hee-haw, hee-haw!"

"Quack! Try again. Try again – quack!" said the ducks. "Just sit down and move your legs about, like this." And they went swimming along to show him how easy it was.

So the little donkey waded out into the pond till the water was up to the top of his legs, then he began to move them about. But he splashed such a lot that all the water flew up in the air!

"Go away!" quacked the ducks. "You're – quack, quack – splashing all the water out of the pond!"

So the little donkey climbed out of the water and sat down on the bank.

"I'm hungry now, after all that swimming," he said. "Hee-haw, can you give me something nice to eat?"

"Quack, quack! We can get you a few nice worms," said the ducks.

"I don't like worms," said the little donkey. "I want some carrots."

"Quack, quack! We haven't got any carrots," said the ducks. "Sorry, little donkey, only worms."

The little donkey got up. "Well," he said, "I don't like the water and I don't like swimming, and I don't like worms. So I shan't try to be a duck any more. I shall just be a little donkey."

And he ran off up the field shouting: "Hee-haw, hee-haw, hee-haw!"

What a funny little donkey!

Paul's Daisies

Joan Cass

Paul had finished his dinner. He was sitting at the table with his father and mother and Frank, his big brother, and Marjorie his big sister. Yes, Paul had finished his dinner, and he wanted to go out, for he had something very special to do. But the others were still eating and talking, so he said: "Mummy, can I go out and play – by myself?"

And his mother said, "Yes, Paul, but put your coat on in case the wind gets cold."

So Paul put on his coat and went out of the front door and down the path, and stood at the gate with his hands in his pockets. It was a lovely day to be out playing – warm and windy. Clouds were blowing across the sky, leaves were moving softly on the trees, and a little bird was singing.

Paul was the only person outside in the whole street.

So he stood there – and thought about the special thing he wanted to do.

Tomorrow was going to be Mother's birthday. He wanted to give her a lovely present.

He had a new tenpenny piece that his grannie had given him. It was in his pocket now.

He knew his father had a present all ready to give Mother. A pair of red bedroom-slippers. And Marjorie and Frank had bought her a box of lacy handkerchiefs.

But what should Paul buy?

The street he lived in wasn't very good for shopping. There were only three very small shops, and then nothing but six very big houses, three on each side of the road, with big, big gardens, and they were all being pulled down so

that new, smaller houses could be built. There were great piles of sand and bricks and wood at the bottom of the street. The workmen were there every day wheeling barrows and mixing mortar.

Paul went each morning to watch the men working.

So now he walked along the road to the first big house to see what was happening. But it was Saturday afternoon and no one was there. The house that was being pulled down had a big garden with tall trees, and Paul could see a long stretch of green grass. Then, when he looked closer, he saw something else.

The long stretch of green grass was just covered with daisies!

Paul began to feel very pleased and excited, because a bunch of daisies was just what his mother would love for a birthday present. He was quite sure of that.

He went into the garden and began picking as fast as he

could, pink-tipped daisies with nice long stalks. When he had picked a big bunch he walked back down the street, wondering what he would do with his new tenpenny piece.

Now, one of the three little shops I told you about was a draper's shop, and Paul suddenly remembered you could buy ribbon there. Some pink ribbon to tie up the daisies would be lovely. He opened the shop door, and went in.

Inside the shop there was a lady standing behind the counter. She knew Paul, so she smiled at him, and said: "What can I do for you, Paul?"

"I want some pink ribbon, please – can you cut me this much worth?" said Paul, and he put his tenpenny piece on the counter.

"I think so," said the drapery-lady, and she measured the ribbon, and cut a piece off, and wrapped it up for him.

Then he took the little parcel and said, "Thank you," and the lady put the money in a drawer under the counter.

Paul hurried off home to put his daisies in water, and hide them away until tomorrow.

Next morning, all Mother's birthday presents were put on the breakfast table. Paul's daisies, tied up with pink ribbon, were lying on her plate. And as soon as Mother saw them, she said: "What specially lovely daisies, and what gay, pink ribbon! Are these from you, Paul?" And she gave him a specially big hug.

"Please look at our presents now, Mummy," said Marjorie and Frank.

Mother opened the box of lacy handkerchiefs and said they were just what she wanted. Then she tried on the red bedroom-slippers, and they fitted her exactly. "What a lovely birthday I'm having," said Mother. Then she sat down and began to pour out the tea.

And Paul smiled to himself, because he knew by the way his mother looked at him that she loved his daisies.

Gregory Goat and the Very Old Duck

Molly Sole

Gregory Goat lived in a big field with a very old duck. The very old duck didn't say much; she would sit for hours and hours just staring at nothing; then perhaps she would suddenly say: "Qua-a-ack."

Now, Gregory Goat was very proud of himself, and he was quite sure that when the old duck was staring she was admiring his fine shape and silky beard. He would walk up and down in front of her, and when at last she suddenly said, "Qua-a-ack," he was sure she was just sighing with pleasure that such a fine creature as he should live in the same field as herself.

And I must tell you that as well as being vain and proud, Gregory Goat was also very greedy. He was always hungry, no matter what he ate or how much he ate. And at meal times he wished that the old duck did not live with him because no matter how fast he gobbled his share of the food the very old duck ate just as quickly and never left any of hers for Gregory.

So Gregory tried to think of some way of having both her company and her food, and one afternoon his eyes began to gleam and he gave a little secret laugh. "Maa-ha-ha," he said because he had thought of a good plan, "Maa-ha-ha."

He thought that if he could keep the very old duck awake all the afternoon she would be so tired by tea-time that she would fall asleep and he would have all the food for himself.

So one day – just as the old duck was settling down for her afternoon nap with a sleepy, "Qua-a-ack," Gregory went very close to her and shouted "Maaa-aa-ah" so loudly that she jumped a little and blinked her eyes. Then Gregory banged on their food plates with his hard hoofs, making a dreadful clatter.

Next he galloped back and forth in front of her, passing so close and so fast that all her feathers were ruffled with the wind he made and his little hard hoofs made a noise like thunder in her ears.

Then he danced all round her on his hind legs waving his front feet in the air in a most dangerous way and as he danced, he sang at the top of his voice:

"I'm Gregory Goat
My beard is fine,
And will you note
This coat of mine?
Maa-ah-ah."

Gregory Goat went on singing and dancing and banging and galloping all the afternoon to keep the very old duck from sleeping. At long last he knew it was getting near tea-time. He was so breathless and worn out with his efforts that he sat down to have a little rest.

He was pleased to see that the very old duck was going off to sleep. "*Nothing* will wake her up now," he thought, and he gave a little chuckle, "Maa-ah-ha."

He even closed his own eyes for a minute and had a little dream about the great big tea he was going to have. At least he *thought* he had only closed his eyes for a minute, but when he opened them it was quite dark and long past tea-time. He jumped up and rushed over to the food plates. They were both empty!

And there, by the light of the stars, he could see the very old duck all tucked up for the night looking *exceedingly* well fed and cosy. Poor silly Gregory Goat! He had made himself so tired with all his leaping and prancing he had been too fast asleep to hear the food coming at tea-time.

The well-fed very old duck slept happily all night long. Sometimes she murmured a happy, "Quaa-aa-ack," in her sleep. Gregory Goat was so hungry that he slept very badly indeed, and said, "Maaaa-aa-ah," every now and again in the most miserable way. But nobody heard him. "Maaaa-aa-aah."

Gregory Goat Tries to Swim

Molly Sole

Now as you know, Gregory Goat was very conceited. He was sure that he could do everything much better than anyone else, and as he never saw anyone but the very old duck he thought he was finer-looking than any other creature. But there was one thing the very old duck could do very well – something Gregory Goat could not do. She could swim on the pond at the end of the field.

Gregory Goat didn't like water. He didn't want to get his lovely beard all wet and dripping, so he had never learnt to swim. And every time the very old duck waddled off to the end of the field and swam boldly round and round the pond, Gregory Goat would go right to the other side of the field and jump and prance and gallop as hard as he could, pretending to take no notice of anything so silly as swimming.

But it worried Gregory Goat to think there was something the very old duck could do which he could not, so one day he decided to watch her when she was swimming.

The old duck woke early from her afternoon sleep that day. She shook out her feathers, said "Quaaaaaa-aaaak," to herself and then waddled very slowly towards the pond. Gregory Goat waited until she had been swimming around for a little while, then he strolled down to the water. All the way there he pretended to be looking for something in the grass. When at last he got to the edge of the pond and looked into the water, he saw something which quite made him forget what he had come for. He saw his own face reflected in the water and he was delighted with what he saw.

He waggled his beard up and down and smiled with pleasure at its beauty. He turned his head this way and that so that he could see the whole length of his horns. Then he bent nearer and nearer to the water so that he could see how lovely his eyes were. He bent down and down and down till suddenly he fell in, head first, with a tremendous splash!

"Maaaa-aaaaa-*aaaaaaa*," shouted Gregory, as soon as his head came up above the water. "Maaa-aaaaa-*aaaaa*." He was so surprised and frightened that he kicked and splashed with all his feet and opened his mouth and shouted "Maaaaaa-aaaaaa-aaaaa," and swallowed a lot of pond water and got in an awful state.

All this time the very old duck had been swimming round and round in her usual dreamy way. But Gregory's splashings made little waves spread out all over the pond. "Dear me," she said, "what's happening?" and then she saw Gregory. "Quaaaaa-aaaak," she said. She paddled slowly over towards him. But when she got near to Gregory, what do you think she did? She caught hold of his lovely long beard with her beak and pulled him slowly to the edge of the water. And then left him to scramble out on to dry land. But she went on swimming round and round as if nothing had happened.

Poor Gregory! There he was, wet all over, full of pond water and his beautiful beard was all thin and wet and straggly. "Maaaaa-aaaa-aaaah," he said in the most miserable way, "Maaaaa-aaaa-aaaa."

It took him the whole of that day and most of the next to forget how foolish he had been. But at last he thought of something which made him feel better. "My beard is not only beautiful," he said to himself, "it is also very useful and very *very* strong." And after that whenever the very old duck swam on the pond, Gregory Goat trotted round and round the edge of the water singing:

"I'm Gregory Goat
My beard is long,
And what is more
It's very strong.
Maaaaaa-aaaaaaaa."

Baby Sparrow

Mary Cockett

When sparrows built a nest up between the pipes outside Paul's bedroom, he was very pleased. He couldn't see the whole nest even when he pressed his face against the window, but he could see bits of straw sticking out from one edge of it.

He couldn't see the mother sparrow sitting on her nest, but he often saw the father sparrow bringing her food. He never saw the eggs, of course, for they were at the bottom of the nest. But when the eggs hatched out, when the baby birds had come out of their shells, he could sometimes *hear* them.

When there wasn't an aeroplane roaring overhead, when there wasn't a car screeching its brakes, when the carpet cleaner wasn't rumbling about in his house, *then* he could hear the baby birds. Often he stood quite still close by the window and listened to their high little voices cheeping for food.

The mother bird and the father bird worked hard all day fetching food for their hungry family. The tiny sparrows grew and grew until one day Paul ran to his mother saying, "I can see little beaks poking over the edge of the nest. The baby birds must be getting big."

"Let's hope they don't fall out," said his mother.

"Yes," said Paul, "they might get killed if they did."

Paul didn't like to think about that, so he went inside and helped his mother to clean the house. While she used the carpet cleaner, he used the floor mop. He liked the long handle, and he liked the fluffy head of the mop that gathered up the dust. "Flippy, floppy soft," he said it was. He liked pushing the floor mop all along the hall. It was like driving some sort of traffic – he wasn't sure what.

That day, when he had finished helping, his mother shook the mop as usual, and then decided to wash it. When it was washed she took it out through the kitchen door and propped it against the coal bunkers, with its flippy, floppy soft top pointing upwards.

She said, "It'll dry there in the sun. Don't touch it, Paul."

Paul didn't touch it. He forgot all about it, and so did his mother. In fact, it stayed out all day and all night and all the next morning.

Paul was in his bedroom playing on the floor. Now and again he heard the baby sparrows chirping, but he had got used to them by now, and he didn't listen very hard.

At least he didn't stop playing to listen until the squawking was so loud that it made him stand up and go to the window. They *were* making a noise. He looked up. Only part of the noise came from up there in the nest, and part of the noise seemed to be down below him. How strange! At first he couldn't understand it.

Then he *did* understand it, for a baby sparrow had fallen from the nest. But it had not fallen on the hard ground. It had been lucky. Can you guess where it had landed? On the upturned floor mop that was now quite dry!

Paul wasn't a minute in getting downstairs. As he went he was calling to his mother, "Hurry, hurry, but don't touch the floor mop. Don't touch it! A baby sparrow's in it!"

His mother opened the kitchen door and looked out. She lifted Paul up so that he could see. There on the flippy, floppy mop, there with its open mouth bigger than

its head, squawked the baby sparrow. It was feeling about with its feet. Big feet they were.

Paul's mother said, "What a shock for the poor little thing, and I don't think it likes our floor mop as a nest."

"Get him out," said Paul.

So Paul's mother lifted out the baby bird and held it in both hands. Up above, the mother sparrow flew round and round, not knowing what to do.

Paul said, "Put her baby on the lawn and then she'll feed it."

But his mother said, "What about cats? It wouldn't take them long to find a baby bird on a lawn, and remember, it can't fly."

Paul shuddered. He had forgotten for a moment about cats. "A cat shan't have it," he said. "We'll take it in the house and feed it."

But the baby bird squawked and squawked. It wanted its mother. It didn't want to go and live in Paul's house. So what were Paul and his mother to do?

I'll tell you what they did. They borrowed a bird cage from Miss Mabel who lived next door and who once long ago had had a canary. The bird cage was lying empty in her cellar, but Miss Mabel was glad to fetch it up and clean it.

Paul made a bed in the cage for the baby sparrow. He made it out of grass and flower petals and his teddy's old jersey. His mother took down the washing line and hung the cage on the hook there on the house wall, where the mother sparrow would see her baby every time she came to the nest.

Then they opened the cage door wide, and Paul's mother fixed wire across the bottom of its doorway so that the baby sparrow couldn't fall out.

Paul said, "Are you sure its mother will come to feed it?"

"No," said his mother, "I'm not sure. We'll go into the house and watch."

And that is what they did. The mother sparrow had been watching them anxiously. Now she saw Paul and his mother go inside and shut the kitchen door. They went up to Paul's room and waited behind the curtain. It was a very short wait luckily. In less than five minutes the mother sparrow flew to the cage with food for her baby. In another minute the father sparrow brought food too. And all day long they fed the babies in the nest and the baby in the cage.

That night Paul was lifted up to put a cover over the cage to keep the sparrow warm and dry in case of rain. For three more days the baby sparrow stayed in the cage, and then can you guess what happened?

It didn't fall out. It flew out. Yes, it had learnt to fly.

Young Mouse and the Drum

Ro Godsland

Young Mouse came skipping over the hill one windy afternoon. The wind blew, "Whoo-oo-oo," ruffling his fur and puffing the big white clouds across the sky. It blew through the tall grass, "Whoo-oo-oo." And Young Mouse with his two little drum sticks played upon his drum. Then he began to march to the beating of his drum rumpety-tum-rumpety-tum. The wind whistled round him, but rumpety-tum he marched over the hill, beating his drum and shouting:

"A rumpety-tum, I'm beating my drum.
A rumpety-tumpety-tumpety-tum."

Old Grandpa Toad heard the noise. He was sweeping the leaves off his garden path, but as fast as he swept them up the wind blew again, and more leaves came fluttering down from the tree. "Bother the leaves," said Grandpa Toad, and he began to thump his broom as he swept the leaves to the beat of Young Mouse's drum. Past the gate came Young Mouse shouting:

"A rumpety-tum, I'm beating my drum.
A rumpety-tumpety-tumpety-tum."

Grandpa Toad put his broom over his shoulder and marched through the gate like a soldier, away down the road behind Young Mouse and his drum. They passed the tree where Mrs Squirrel had her home. She was combing her children's bushy tails. The little squirrels were making a great fuss about it and squeaking: "Oo, you hurt me," and, "Ow, that's a knot," and Mrs Squirrel was getting rather cross.

"Hark!" said one of the children suddenly. "There's a band," and they all ran out of the hole in the tree to look. And then they saw Young Mouse and Grandpa Toad walking past.

"A rumpety-tum, I'm beating my drum.
A rumpety-tumpety-tumpety-tum."

The little squirrels scrambled down the tree and fell into line behind Grandpa Toad singing, "Rumpety-tumpety-tumpety-tum."

Mrs Squirrel came running after her children, scolding and waving her comb.

Now Miss Duck was hanging out her tablecloth to dry in the garden. "Whoever is making all that noise?" she said. Then she saw Young Mouse and Grandpa Toad, and the little squirrels and Mrs Squirrel all marching in a straight line along the road. Miss Duck ran to her gate and called: "Where are you going? Where are you going?"

But all Young Mouse would say was:

"A rumpety-tum, I'm beating my drum.
A rumpety-tumpety-tumpety-tum."

Well, they all looked so jolly and seemed so happy that Miss Duck ran out into the road crying "Wait for me! Wait for me!" and she joined on behind Mrs Squirrel waving her tablecloth like a flag. Up over the hill they all marched, following Young Mouse and his drum.

"A rumpety-tumpety-tumpety-tum," sang Young Mouse. Mrs Squirrel beat time with her comb, and Miss Duck's tablecloth flapped in the wind like a big flag.

What a fine band it was marching up over the hill on that windy afternoon!

Over the top of the hill they came and down the other side. Then all of a sudden the wind blew a black rain cloud in front of the sun. Plip-plop, plip-plop, the raindrops began to fall, faster and faster.

"Home. We must hurry home," called Mrs Squirrel, and she found her children and hustled them in front of her and away went the squirrels running and leaping until they were safely back in their tree house. The wind had blown all the tangles out of the little squirrels' tails and they were as hungry as hunters. So they all sat down and had bread and jam and milk for tea, and then Mrs Squirrel read them a story.

"Home," said Miss Duck. "I must go home." And she turned and waddled off. The wind had blown her tablecloth dry, so when she reached her kitchen she ironed it and spread it on the table, and made herself a nice cup of tea.

"Home," puffed Grandpa Toad, and he hurried off leaning on his broom to help him along. When he got to his garden gate he saw that the path was quite clean and tidy, for the wind had blown all the leaves away. So he sat inside his porch looking at the rain, and smoked a pipe and sang, "Pom-pom-pom-pom," to himself, thumping his foot on the doorstep.

As for Young Mouse, he stayed where he was when he felt the spots of rain and curled up small beneath his drum and slept there, snug and dry, until the sun came out again.

The Wooden Horse

Violet Statham

Once upon a time there was a little wooden horse. When he was new he was black and white with a silky mane and long tail – and he had bright red reins. But now he was old, so his paint was scratched and dull and his mane and tail were very thin.

He belonged to a boy who was called Tony, and they had played together since Tony was a baby. And that was a long time ago.

So the little wooden horse was one of Tony's oldest friends. There were so many new toys at Christmas time that Mother said: "I'm going to put some of your old toys up in the attic, children!" And the children were so busy playing with their new toys and reading their new books, that they didn't mind Mother taking their old toys away.

Mother carried the little wooden horse up and up and up the stairs to the top of the house. Then she opened the door of the attic room just under the roof where she kept old boxes and things, and she left him on the floor by the little window. Then she went away and shut the door.

It was very quiet in the attic room. And it was cold. No children came up there to play. And there was no fire to make it warm. So there the little wooden horse stayed till six days after Christmas were gone.

On the seventh day after Christmas the little wooden horse woke up and looked out of the window. It was snowing, and oh, so cold!

"Brrr," said the little wooden horse. "Oh dear, will

Tony never come and take me down to play with him again? Brr," he said again. "It's cold up here. I wish I had something to cover me up."

A fat old spider walked across the floor and said: "Cold, are you? I'll soon cover you up."

And she set to work and spun a web round and round the little wooden horse. All that day she worked, spinning and spinning a fine grey web.

"You're very kind," said the little wooden horse. "What a fine grey cover you are making for me, to be sure."

"And it will be warm," said the fat old spider, "for it is made of the finest silk." She went on spinning and weaving till the little wooden horse was wrapped all over in a fine grey silken cover.

"Thank you, spider," he said. "Oh, I feel warmer and happier now. It won't be so bad being up here if you'll come and talk to me now and again." Then the little wooden horse snuggled cosily into his silken coat and soon went fast asleep.

Now that very night Tony remembered his little wooden horse, and when he was going to bed he said: "Mummy, where is my little wooden horse? I want him and I can't find him."

"He's in the attic," said his mother. "You can get him in the morning." And she kissed him goodnight and went downstairs.

But Tony couldn't go to sleep. He kept thinking and thinking about his old friend, the little wooden horse, and he wanted to have him there beside his bed. At last Tony got out of bed, up and up and up the stairs he went, and he opened the door of the attic room. And there, what did he see looking like silver in the moonlight? The little wooden horse, wrapped in a soft silken web. Tony ran to the window and picked him up and said: "I'm sorry I forgot you, wooden horse. I'll never forget you again."

He took him down and down and down the stairs. He set him beside his bed and kissed him and patted him and said: "Goodnight, little horse. See you in the morning." Then he got into bed and fell fast asleep.

And the little horse was so proud and happy he felt like prancing for joy. But he never forgot about the friendly old spider, even though he was so pleased to be playing with Tony again.

The Puss, the Puss with the Fine Golden Basket

Leila Berg

Once upon a time there were two little children. One day they were very hungry, so the little boy said: "I will go to the baker's to buy some bread. And you, little girl, go to the greengrocer's to buy some red apples. And the pussycat must go to the dairy and bring back some milk."

So the two children tied a golden basket round the pussycat's neck and sent her off to the dairy for the milk.

And the little boy went off to the baker's for the bread.

And the little girl went off to the greengrocer's for the red apples.

By and by the little boy came back with the bread. And he cut it up in slices.

And by and by the little girl came back with the apples. And she peeled them and cut them up in pieces.

But pussycat hadn't come back.

No puss, no puss, with the fine golden basket.

So the little boy and the little girl called to the dog. And they said to him:

"Dog, dog, pussy's not home,
"No puss, no puss, with the fine golden basket.
"Bite her long tail and send her back home!"

But the dog said no, no, he wouldn't.

And there was no puss, no puss, with the fine golden basket.

So the children called the horse. And they said to him:

"Horse, horse, pussy's not home,
No puss, no puss, with the fine golden basket.
Trot off with your cart, and bring her back home!"

But the horse said nay, nay, he wouldn't.

And *still* there was no puss, no puss, with the fine golden basket.

So the children called the motor car. And they said to it:

"Motor car, motor car, pussy's not home.
No puss, no puss, with the fine golden basket.
Go quick as you can and bring her back home!"

But the car said peep-peep, and wouldn't.

And *still* there was no puss, no puss, with the fine golden basket.

So the children called Timothy Trot. And they said to him:

"Timothy Trot, pussy's not home.
No puss, no puss, with the fine golden basket.
Just jump in the car and drive her back home!"

And Timothy Trot jumped up and said: "Oh, what a

fine idea. I *like* driving cars." And he jumped quickly inside, pressed the starter, and at once the car went brr-brr-brr.

"Peep-peep, we're off," said the car.

And away they went – Timothy Trot and the car – down the road they went till they met the horse.

And they gave him a teeny-weeny bump – *boof*, like that – just to teach him to hurry.

And the horse got such a fright, off he galloped – clippety-clop – to find the dog. Clippety-clop, clippety-clop he went till he met the dog.

And he gave the dog just a teeny-weeny kick – *klick-klack* – like that – just to teach him to hurry.

And the dog got such a fright, off he went tearing down the road to find the cat. The puss, the puss, with the fine golden basket. She was there all right. She sat on a wall washing her face.

Then the dog said: "Puss, puss, come at once, or I will bite your furry tail!"

So puss jumped off the wall and ran up the road. And behind her dashed the dog – wuff-wuff.

And behind him galloped the horse – clippety-clop, clippety-clop.

And behind him raced the car – brr-brr-brr – with Timothy Trot sitting inside, tooting the horn – Peep-peep!

What a long, long line that was, running up the road!

And that is how the puss, the puss, with the fine golden basket came home with the milk at last.

David and the Window Cleaner

Vera Colwell

"Oh dear!" sighed David. "I've got nothing to do."

"You have lots of toys," said his mother. "Why not play with your engine? Even if you have a cold, you can have fun."

"I don't want to play with anything," grumbled David. "Isn't anything exciting happening today, Mummy?"

"Well," answered his mother. "Let me see. The baker's coming, and he may have some iced buns."

"Goodie!" said David. "I like iced buns."

"Then Mrs Brown is coming to help me and we are having sausages and treacle tart for dinner."

"I *like* treacle tart," said David.

"Oh, and this afternoon," continued his mother, "the window cleaner's coming."

"Hurrah!" shouted David. "Can I help him?"

"Not outside, I'm afraid, David. There's a cold wind."

David was disappointed. He liked going out and talking to the window cleaner, and sometimes going with him to the other houses in the street.

The morning passed and David still felt unhappy, but the baker coming with the iced buns cheered him up a bit, and the treacle tart for dinner made him feel nearly happy because it was his favourite pudding.

Then the window cleaner came knocking on the back door. David ran to answer it.

"Hello, young man," said the window cleaner. "Are you coming out with me today?"

"I can't," said David. "I've got a cold."

"Never mind. I'll fill my bucket with water at the kitchen tap here while you run upstairs. Ask your Mum if she'll give you a duster to take with you – and mind you watch for me at the right window."

David rushed upstairs as fast as he could with the duster in his hand. He went into his mother's room first – no window cleaner. He ran along to his own room and looked through that window. There down below was the window cleaner with his ladder. And there was Toby the dog, following him about.

The window cleaner put his ladder against the wall, and made it grow longer and longer. Up and up it came until it reached the bedroom window. Then up came the window cleaner himself. David was pressing his face close against the window when suddenly – "Caught you!" called the window cleaner – and he pretended to catch David's nose with his duster.

David chuckled with delight. "Do it again!" he laughed. "Do it again!" He had a good time running from one room to another to find the window cleaner. Sometimes he tried to clean the window inside with *his* duster as fast as the man cleaned it outside, but he could never manage it. He laughed and jumped about, and felt really happy at last.

The window cleaner polished all the windows upstairs until they shone. He had finished the last one and was just shaking his cloth when it slipped out of his hand. Down it fell and landed right on dog Toby's nose. He did look funny!

He shook his head and pulled at the duster until it fell off, and then the window cleaner climbed down the ladder and picked it up.

David ran downstairs into the room where his mother was sitting. The window cleaner was outside cleaning the window there. David could hear some music. He looked to see where it came from. The radio wasn't on. Neither was the television. "Where's the music, Mummy?" he asked.

The window cleaner heard him through the open window, and laughed. He pointed to a little box that was slung on a strap to his back and he began pretending to sing.

"He's got a tiny little radio!" said David.

"Whatever next!" said his mother.

And now the window cleaner had finished. He switched off the little radio, folded up his ladder, wrung out his cloth and threw away the dirty water.

"Take this money to him, please David," said his mother, "and say thank you!"

"Goodbye, Mr Window Cleaner," said David. "I like you – we have fun! Come again soon!"

Three Little Bunnies who Lost their Mummies

Valerie Beales

There were once three little bunnies who were playing at jumping in and out of holes with their mummies. Suddenly they lost their mummies. They came jumping out of three little holes and they couldn't find their mummies anywhere! Think of that.

Well, those three little bunnies were very sad, of course. They wandered about, looking for their mummies, and calling for their mummies. "Mummy! Mummy!" they called. But their mummies never came. What a to-do!

When they had wandered quite a long way they met three big dogs. "Please, have you seen our mummies?" asked the three little bunnies.

"No, we haven't, and we chase little rabbits," said the three big dogs. "Gr-r-r-r!" And they chased those three little bunnies all along the road. The little bunnies ran as fast as they could away from the dogs. Oh, how fast they ran!

And then they went on looking for their mummies.

Soon they met three large cows. "Please, have you seen our mummies?" asked the three little bunnies.

"No, we haven't," said the three large cows. "And we poke little rabbits with our horns. Moo-oo-oo!" Then they tried to poke them with their horns, and the three little bunnies ran away as fast as they could.

They went on and on, looking for their mummies, and feeling very unhappy.

Then they met three large birds. "Please, have you seen our mummies?" asked the three little bunnies.

"What do your mummies look like?" asked the birds.

"My mummy's got one white ear and one brown ear," said the first little rabbit.

"My mummy's got very, very long whiskers," said the second little rabbit.

"My mummy's got four white paws," said the third little rabbit.

"Well," said the birds, "we've seen three big rabbits just like that sitting behind the wood over there, all in a row, crying."

"Oh! Those must be our mummies," said the three little bunnies. "Perhaps they are crying because they've lost us."

"Well, jump on our backs," said the kind birds, "and we'll take you there."

So the three little bunnies jumped on to the backs of the three kind birds and held tight, and away they flew, over the wood, to where the three mummy rabbits were sitting in a row, crying. The three birds flew down and landed in a row right in front of the mummy rabbits.

"When they looked up and saw their little bunnies all safe and sound they *were* pleased. They hugged them and they hugged them, and then they thanked the three kind birds very much for bringing them home.

"You must be hungry," said the mummy rabbits. "We've got dinner all ready for you. Come along and see what we've got."

And what do you think they had for dinner? They had carrots, and cottage pie, and apples and custard. And then before they said goodbye, the mother bunnies gave each of the three kind birds a nice, fat, juicy worm.

Cold Paws

Dorothy Dixon

Pussy White was a lovely white pussy with pale blue eyes and a pretty little pink nose. She lived by herself in a teeny-weeny cottage, just big enough for a pussy who lived all alone.

She was a very happy pussy, but she had one big bother – her paws were always cold. "I like a cold nose," she said, "but I do *not* like cold paws."

One day, when her paws felt extra cold, Pussy White said to herself: "I wonder how other pussies keep their paws warm? I must go and find out."

So she went to see her friend Pussy Black.

"Good morning, Pussy Black. My paws are very cold. How can I warm them?"

"Well," said Pussy Black, "when *my* paws are cold I stretch them out in front of the fire and *that* warms them."

"Thank you, Pussy Black. That *is* a good idea," said Pussy White.

So she went home and put a big shovelful of coal on the fire. Then she lay down in front of it and stretched out her paws. And they got beautifully warm.

After a time Pussy White felt hungry, so she went to the larder to get a plate of fish. And before she had finished her dinner her paws felt quite cold again. "Oh dear," she said, "this won't do. I must go and find out how other pussies keep their paws warm *all* the time."

So she went to see her friend Pussy Grey.

"Good afternoon, Pussy Grey. When I eat my dinner my paws get very cold. How can I warm them?"

"Well," said Pussy Grey, "when *my* paws are cold I put them in a basin of hot water and *that* warms them."

"Thank you, Pussy Grey. That *is* a good idea," said Pussy White.

So she went home and filled the kettle with water and put it on the fire. When the water was warm she poured it into a big basin.

"OO-ouch, that's hot!" said Pussy White, when she stepped into the basin. Soon her paws got beautifully warm.

But when the water turned cool her paws felt quite cold again. So she dried them carefully and went to see her friend, Pussy Ginger.

"Good evening, Pussy Ginger. My paws are very cold. How can I warm them?"

"Well," said Pussy Ginger, "when *my* paws are cold I run round and round the garden and *that* warms them."

"Thank you, Pussy Ginger. That *is* a good idea," said Pussy White.

So she went home and ran round and round the garden. It was a teeny-weeny garden so she ran round it ten times. Her paws got beautifully warm.

All that running had made her thirsty, so she went to the larder to get a saucer of milk. But before she had finished her milk her paws felt quite cold again.

"Oh dear, I'm afraid I shall have to go on having cold paws for ever and ever," thought poor Pussy White sadly.

Now all Pussy White's friends – Pussy Black, Pussy Grey and Pussy Ginger, were very sorry about her cold paws.

"Poor Pussy White," said Pussy Black. "However do her paws get so cold?"

"I know," said Pussy Grey, "it is because her cottage has a stone floor and when she walks about on it of course her paws get cold!"

"Then we must knit her some boots," said Pussy Ginger.

But there were only three friends and Pussy White had four cold paws. So Pussy Ginger, who was the best knitter, promised to make two boots.

"Who has any wool?" asked Pussy Black.

"I have enough blue wool to knit three blue boots," said Pussy Grey.

"And I have enough pink wool to knit one pink boot," said Pussy Ginger.

"I have no wool, but I have lots and lots of knitting needles," said Pussy Black.

So they all began to knit, and were very busy, I can tell you.

A few weeks later there was a rat-tat-tat on Pussy White's door. Pussy White ran and opened the door and there stood the postman with a little parcel.

"Are you sure it is for me?" asked Pussy White. "I have never had a parcel before."

"Yes, it must be for you," said the postman, "because it

says 'Miss Pussy White, Cream Cottage' on the outside. Look!" and he gave her the parcel.

What could it be? Can you guess? Pussy White's paws shook with excitement as she opened the parcel. Inside were four lovely little blue boots with pink tops. That was clever Pussy Ginger's idea. She thought four blue boots with pink tops would look much nicer then three blue boots and one pink boot.

I think so too. Don't you?

There was a letter pinned on to the boots. It said:

"*Dear Pussy White,*

We hope these boots will warm your cold paws.

With love from,

Pussy Black, Pussy Grey and Pussy Ginger."

Pussy White *was* pleased. "What dear little boots," she said. "The blue is as blue as my eyes, and the pink is as pink as my nose. What kind friends I have!"

And she put them on at once, and now her four paws are always as warm as toast.

The Shiny Buttons

Joy Tucker

Jenny had a new coat. She had it for her birthday. It was red and very nice, and it fastened with four beautiful buttons. Jenny knew that there were four buttons because it was the same number as the candles on her birthday cake. She had counted the candles before she blew them out – one, two, three, four – and then, a big puff, and all the candles had gone out.

Jenny liked to blow at the buttons on her new coat too, for they were bright and shiny, like new pennies. When she breathed on them they would stop shining for a moment until she rubbed them with a little piece of cotton-wool from her mother's bandage-box, and then they would shine brightly again.

One day, Jenny's mother said: "You can put your new coat on today, Jenny, when we go to tea with Grandma." So Jenny puffed and blew on the buttons and rubbed them till they were very shiny indeed, and her mother said: "Grandma will say you look very smart in your new coat."

The bus which went to the street where Jenny's grandmother lived was exactly the same shade of red as Jenny's new coat. Jenny and her mother sat on the front seat all the way and Jenny's buttons made four little lights on the window of the bus. The little lights kept still when Jenny kept still, and jumped about when she jumped about. It was quite a long way to Grandma's house, and Jenny was pleased when Mother said: "We get off at the next stop."

They hurried along the street and soon saw Jenny's grandmother waiting at her door. The first thing she said was: "You do look smart in your new coat, Jenny – but oh dear! You've lost a button!"

Jenny looked down at her coat and started to count the buttons – one, two, three – and that was all! Where the other button had been there was only a dangling thread! Jenny felt very sad, especially when Mother said: "It must have come off in the bus – what a pity! I don't think I have another one the same."

But Grandma said: "Never mind, after tea Jenny can look in my button-box and perhaps she'll find one to match."

When tea was over, Grandma went to the cupboard and took out a large tin box. It had pictures of flowers all over it and it made a rattling noise. Jenny opened the lid and looked inside. She had never *seen* so many buttons. There were big buttons and little buttons, hard buttons and soft buttons, red, green, blue and yellow buttons, and some buttons in colours that Jenny didn't even know.

Yet, although she looked and looked, she could not find any shiny buttons. Jenny's mother looked, too, but there was not a shiny gold button to be seen.

But Grandma said: "I'm sure there's one there – ah, yes, here it is," and she picked out a button from the bottom of the box. It wasn't shiny at all – but dull and dark. "Wait a minute," said Grandma, and she went out to her kitchen and came back carrying a little piece of cotton-wool which had some pink soapy stuff on it. "This will do the trick."

And she rubbed and rubbed at the dull, dark button and, like magic, it began to shine. Soon it was gleaming like the other buttons on Jenny's new coat. And before they went home, Mother snipped off the loose thread where the lost button had been, and sewed on the button from Grandma's box in its place.

Going home in the bus, Jenny sat very still so that she could count the little lights that her buttons made in the window – one, two, three, four – and she was glad that Grandma had found the spare button in her box and made it shine like the others on her coat. And the four little lights twinkled at Jenny all the way home.

The House that was High and Dry

Joan Gambrell

Freddy and Fanny Fieldmouse lived in a neat little hole in the bank of earth at the side of a cornfield. The bank was covered with grass and wild flowers, and had a hedge growing along the top, and a dry ditch at the bottom.

Freddy had worked hard with his pink feet and his sharp nose to dig a smooth tunnel in the earth, with a round room at the end. Fanny had tidied up the entrance, and made a curtain of grass and leaves to hide the front door from the sharp eyes of Mr Owl who lived in the wood nearby, and of any other person who might wish to harm them. Now all was neat and tidy, and the two little mice sat in their living-room at the end of the passage, feeling tired but happy.

"What a nice little house we have, my dear!" said Freddy, looking round with pride.

"Yes indeed," agreed Fanny, "and in such a good place too! Just by the cornfield and the wood, so that we shall always have plenty to eat."

The little fieldmice were so tired after their busy day that they soon curled themselves up nose to tail on a bed of soft dry leaves, and fell fast asleep.

While they slept, the night grew very dark outside. Big black rain clouds covered the moon and the wind began to blow so hard that all the trees in the wood swished their branches together, and the young corn in the cornfield was flattened to the ground.

Freddy stirred, and stretched his sleepy paw. "What a stormy night," he murmured and, snuggling down still further in his cosy bed, he went to sleep again.

Fanny woke too, and listened to the wind and the rain that had begun to pitter-patter on the leaves of the hedge above their home. "How wet and cold it must be outside! I am sorry for anyone who has to be out on such a night!" Then she, too, shut her eyes and went to sleep till morning.

When daylight came, the two little fieldmice woke up, scampered along the passage to their front door, and looked out. The big black clouds were still sending down the rain and the wind was still lashing the branches of the trees in the wood. A big raindrop fell *plop!* onto Fanny's nose and made her sneeze.

"Come back inside, quickly!" she called to Freddy, who had parted the leafy curtain and was peering down to the bottom of the bank, his pink nose twitching with excitement.

He came back into the shelter of the passage, and began to brush off the raindrops from his face and whiskers. "My dear!" he said, giving his left ear a quick rub with his paw. "I distinctly saw quite a depth of water in the ditch at the bottom of our bank! Yesterday it was as dry as a bone! What a good thing we dug our house so high up in the bank, or we might have been flooded out!"

"Oh dear, Freddy!" said his wife. "Don't *think* of such a thing! Our beautiful home filled with water? That would be dreadful," and she looked most distressed.

"Now, now, my dear," said Freddy, "didn't I say we were high up in the bank? No need for alarm! You know I am a very clever mouse, and I realised when we chose this place that the farmer had not dug a ditch at the bottom of the bank for nothing. Oh no! It is to collect the water that drains off the cornfield. Where there's a ditch, there will be water sometimes, I said to myself, so I made our hole high up in the bank – and here we are high and dry!" And he curled his tail and twirled his whiskers and looked very knowing.

"Oh Freddy!" said his wife. "You are indeed a clever mouse," and they both trotted back into their living-room and had breakfast together, as contented a pair of mice as you would find in all the countryside.

All through that day it kept on raining, and once every hour Freddy Fieldmouse would scamper along to the front door and peer down at the water in the ditch below, and every time he came back, he would say: "Quite an inch higher my dear!" or: "Rising steadily!" and he would preen his whiskers and think how wise he had been to make their home so high up in the bank. "High and dry! My father always taught me that – high and dry. And I have never forgotten it."

The next morning when the little fieldmice looked out, what a shock they had! The water in the ditch had risen still further during the night and now it was only about six inches away from their front door!

"Oh dear, oh dear," cried Fanny. "I *do* wish it would

stop raining!" And Freddy muttered something that sounded like – "Might have to swim for it yet!"

The water had begun to flow along the ditch now, and pieces of stick and straw floated merrily along it, bouncing against the bank and stopping for a moment, till they were caught up again in the stream, and carried away.

As the two little fieldmice were having their dinner, they heard a sound which made them prick up their ears.

"Help!" said a thin little voice. "Help!"

"Quick!" shouted Freddy, and he dashed along the passage to the front door, with Fanny scampering close behind him.

"Help!" came the cry again, and there they saw a little baby mouse floating down the stream, holding on tightly to a large twig that bobbed along with the current. The twig swirled towards the hole in the bank where Freddy and Fanny stood. Suddenly Freddy turned his back to the stream and put out his long tail into the water.

"Grab my tail and hold on!" he called. The baby mouse let go of the twig and made a grab for Freddy's tail. He clutched it so tightly that Freddy cried out a loud: "Ow!"

Fanny reached over and pulled the little mouse to the bank and safely onto dry land. There he stood, dripping and shivering, while the twig went bouncing on its way.

In no time at all, Fanny had hurried the little wet baby indoors and rubbed him dry. Then she gave him some dinner while Freddy busied himself preparing a cosy bed of dried grass next to their own, and the little one was soon curled up there, safe and warm and dry.

As Freddy and Fanny stood watching him, there was a burst of singing from outside.

"It's Mrs Hedge-Sparrow," said Fanny. "She's telling everyone that the rain has stopped and the sun is shining again."

Freddy scampered off to see for himself, and sure enough there was blue sky overhead and already the water in the ditch was lower. Their home was safe! "High and dry," murmured Freddy to himself. "That's the way to build a house – high and dry."

He ran all the way back to tell Fanny the good news, and found her still looking down at the wee mouse fast asleep in his cosy bed. She looked up at Freddy and said: "He shall stay with us and we will look after him. We will call him Francis. And now that he has come to share it, I think this is the most beautiful home in all the world!"

The Big Blue Removal Van
Vera Rushbrooke

Simon and Emma, and their Mammy and Daddy, were moving out of their old house into a new house. A big blue removal van came to the door to take the furniture to their new home.

The men got out of their van and came into the house. One of the men was called Bill, and the other was called Fred. They went upstairs to bring down the furniture. First they brought down Mammy's best dressing-table. The dressing-table thought a great deal about itself, because it was always being polished, and people used to look at it and say: "What a beautiful dressing-table! What dainty legs! And what a splendid looking-glass!"

As the men carried it downstairs, the dressing-table cried out: "Be careful! Mind you don't break my legs! Don't break my looking-glass, I'll be spoiled if you do! What's the good of a dressing-table without a looking-glass!"

But the men didn't hear what it was saying, they just pushed it into the big removal van and covered it over with cloths. Then the men went upstairs again, and Simon and Emma watched them bringing down a great, old chest of drawers. The chest was grumbling and creaking.

"Well I never! Fancy being pushed and shoved at my age! I'm too old to be dragged up and down stairs!"

And the chest creaked and groaned as the men bumped it down from one stair to another. Bump! Bump! Bump! And then into the big blue removal van it went.

Then upstairs the men went again and brought down all the beds and carpets and put *them* into the big blue removal van.

Then they went into the downstairs room, and while Simon and Emma sat on the stairs and watched, they began moving out the piano.

The piano ran on wheels, so it was easy to move, but it was rather difficult getting it out of the door. The piano began to get fidgety.

"Be careful! I cost an awful lot of money! I mustn't be scratched!"

But the men just huffed and puffed, and pushed and shoved, and said:

"A little to the right, Fred!"

"A little to the left, Bill!"

At last they got it into the big, blue removal van.

"Now the sideboard!" said Fred.

"Have all the cups and saucers and plates been taken out?" asked Bill.

"Yes!" said Fred, tugging at the sideboard. "I'll take this end, and you take the other." And they pushed and pulled, and scrapped and scuffled. The sideboard was old and bad-tempered.

"Be careful! Look out! My door's swinging open! Mind my head doesn't catch in the door!"

And the sideboard nagged and nagged all the way to the big blue removal van.

"The grandfather clock next," said Bill.

"All right," said Fred.

"It's terribly heavy!" said Bill.

Simon and Emma sat on the stairs and laughed.

The grandfather clock's brass face smiled and smiled. "Get a move on," he said, in a deep, deep voice. "I don't want to waste any time!"

At last, Bill and Fred got the grandfather clock into the big blue removal ban.

"Let's take that big box of kettles and pans next," said Fred.

They picked it up, and all the kettles and pans bounced up and down, and clattered and clanged, and giggled and chattered, and were very excited about everything. They quite enjoyed the change, and didn't much care where they were going. So into the big blue removal van they went.

On the mantelpiece was a great big vase.

"I'll take this," said Fred. He carried it out to the big blue removal van, and all the time the vase kept saying:

"If you drop me I shall smash to pieces! Then see what you'll get! Nobody is allowed to touch me!"

But Bill didn't care, he just wrapped the vase in a cloth and put it in the big blue removal van among the rest of the things.

The last to go was the cooker, and it was very angry.

"Nobody cares about me!" it complained. "They don't bother about me till the last minute, and I work harder than any of them! I cook their dinners, and fry their breakfasts, and toast their bread. Yet I'm left to the last!"

But the men just tugged and pulled and shoved and pushed till they got the cooker into the van.

"Let's have a cup of tea now," said Bill, "after all that hard work."

So Bill and Fred had a cup of tea, then they shut the doors of the big blue removal van. Bill climbed into the driver's seat, with Fred beside him. Then with a roar and a rattle, off went the van down the road.

Simon and Emma watched it go. Then Daddy said, "Get into the car children, we must follow the furniture van to our new house."

"Goodbye, old house!" they cried. Then away they went, following the big blue removal van.

Three Little Hens

Elizabeth Gardner

When three hens go out to feed,
Number one is sure to lead,
Number two will come behind,
Number three the last you'll find,
When three hens go out to feed,
Number one is sure to lead.

Nora and Dora and Flora were three little hens and they all lived in Henhouse Lane.

Nora was a black hen, and she lived at Number One in a little black house with a red door.

Dora was a white hen, and she lived at Number Two in a little white house with a yellow door.

But Flora was a speckled hen, and she lived at Number Three in a black-and-white house with a black door.

Every day these three little hens went for a walk together. Nora first, Dora second, and Flora last of all, just like the three little hens in the rhyme.

"Cackle, cackle, it is right and proper that I go first," said black Nora, "for I am the eldest."

"Cackle, cackle, and it is right and proper that I come second," said white Dora, "for I am the second eldest."

"Cackle, cackle, and it is right and proper that I come last," said little speckled Flora, "for I am the youngest."

Nora always carried a black umbrella when they went walking. Dora always carried a white sunshade when they went walking. But little Flora, well, she carried the shopping-basket.

Now, one morning, black Nora looked out of her window and said: "Cackle, cackle, it is a lovely day. We'll go for a picnic." So she put on her black bonnet and away she went.

And white Dora looked out of her window and said: "Cackle, cackle, it is a lovely day. We'll go for a picnic." And she put on her white bonnet and away she went.

Little speckled Flora wasted no time looking out of her window. For she was too busy packing the picnic basket with seed sandwiches and seed cakes. At last she was ready, so she grabbed her speckled bonnet and scurried down the road after Nora and Dora carrying the picnic basket.

"It is going to rain," said black Nora. And she put up her black umbrella. And white Dora walked beside her, underneath it.

So Nora and Dora were sheltered from the rain. But poor little speckled Flora had to walk behind, and the big raindrops dripped off the umbrella and trickled down her poor little back.

"Stop treading on our heels," said Nora and Dora. So poor little speckled Flora had to walk so far behind that the umbrella didn't cover her at all.

Soon the rain stopped and the sun came out. Black Nora shut her umbrella and white Dora put her sunshade up and black Nora walked beside her underneath the sunshade. So Nora and Dora were sheltered from the sun, but poor little Flora had to walk so far behind for fear of treading on their heels that she got no shelter at all. But she was glad, for the warm sun dried the raindrops off her back.

After a while they came to a place where there was a little stream and thousands of buttercups and daisies in the thick green grass.

"Cackle, cackle, we'll have our picnic here," said black Nora.

"Yes, cackle, cackle, this is just the place for a picnic," said white Dora.

"Oh, I'm glad we're going to stop here," said little speckled Flora.

So they had their picnic, and the seed sandwiches and the seed cakes were *lovely*. When they had finished eating, they wandered about the meadow gathering buttercups and daisies, black Nora first, white Dora second, and speckled Flora last of all.

After that they paddled in the stream, and when they were tired they lay down under the big trees and watched the blue sky through the green leaves so high and far away.

At last black Nora got up and said: "We must be going home," and she set off.

"Yes, it's time for us to go," said white Dora, and she set off.

"I'll just pack the cups and spoons in the basket, then I'll follow you," said little speckled Flora – and she did.

"We'll come here for another picnic tomorrow," said black Nora.

"Yes, we'll come here for a picnic tomorrow," said white Dora.

"Oh yes, *let's* come here for another picnic tomorrow," said little speckled Flora.

And they did.

Flora is First

Elizabeth Gardner

The three little hens, black Nora, white Dora and little speckled Flora, were much too busy now to go for picnics. In their houses at Number One, Number Two, and Number Three Henhouse Lane, they each had a nest full of eggs.

Everyone knew about Nora's eggs and Dora's eggs; but no one knew about Flora's eggs.

"Cackle, cackle, I have laid twelve eggs," shouted Nora proudly. "And I shall have twelve fine black chicks."

"Cackle, cackle, I have laid ten eggs," shouted Dora proudly. "And I shall have ten fine white chicks."

But little Flora said nothing at all, for she had only laid six eggs.

"Cackle, cackle, what a lovely morning it is," said Nora looking out of her window one day. "I'm tired of sitting on these eggs. I need a change. I think I'll go for a picnic."

"Cackle, cackle, yes," agreed white Dora, looking out of her window. "We mothers do need a change. No harm will come to the eggs while we are away."

So black Nora put on her black bonnet and took up her black umbrella and white Dora put on her white bonnet and took up her white sunshade; and out they walked into the lane.

"Speckled Flora, speckled Flora," they called together, "come, join us in a picnic. It's a lovely day."

"I'd like to," smiled little Flora, "but I really can't leave my eggs. They would get cold."

"What nonsense!" clucked Nora.

"Sheer laziness!" exclaimed Dora. And off they strutted down the lane.

"Wait, wait," panted Flora, running after them. "I have some sandwiches and seed cake that I was going to have for my dinner. You take them, please."

The black hen and the white hen did not even say, "Thank you". They were too busy arguing.

"Cackle, cackle. *You* carry the basket," said Nora to Dora.

"Cackle, cackle. No. *You* carry the basket," replied Dora to Nora.

So, while they argued, little speckled Flora put the basket down between them and hurried back to her eggs.

Nora and Dora asked a little pig to carry the basket for them and, after a picnic in a meadow, they came home late.

Every day after that they went for a picnic, but every day little Flora stayed at home to sit on her six speckled eggs. She always made her friends sandwiches and seed cake, though, to take with them, and they always took the basket from her without as much as saying, "Thank you".

Well, one morning early, Nora popped her black head out of the window and exclaimed: "Cackle, cackle! What a noise! Where is it all coming from?"

"Yes, indeed, what a noise!" answered Dora popping out her head. "Cackle, cackle. Whatever can it be?"

Just then little speckled Flora ran out of her house looking so happy and excited.

"Nora, Dora," she exclaimed joyously. "My babies have all hatched out of the eggs. Come quickly and see."

When Nora and Dora went into Flora's house they saw six of the loveliest little speckled chicks you could ever dream of. They were all cheeping and squeaking merrily round their mother who was as pleased as could be.

"I can't understand why our eggs haven't hatched," exclaimed Nora angrily.

"Because you haven't been sitting on them, dears," said Flora gently. "You really must, you know, if they are to hatch out."

Well, every morning after that, speckled Flora proudly took her little speckled family for a picnic in the meadow. But Nora and Dora sat at home on their eggs.

"Cackle, cackle. I'll show her," sulked Nora. "She has only six chicks, but soon I'll have twelve."

"Cackle, cackle. I'll show her," muttered Dora. "She has only six chicks and soon I'll have ten."

But, though Nora sat for days and days, only two eggs hatched. And though Dora sat for days and days, only one egg hatched.

Nora and Dora were so ashamed that they would not come out of their houses at all until little Flora came to fetch them.

"Cackle, cackle. Why, these are two beautiful black chicks," she said to Nora. "And that is a most beautiful white one," she added to Dora.

"Come, join us in our picnic," she smiled. "With your chicks and my chicks all scampering together, no one will know which of us they belong to."

So they all went to the meadow for a picnic. But this time little Flora did not make up the sandwiches or carry the basket. Oh, no. Her little chicks would not let her. They prepared the picnic themselves. Then they made her walk first, while they took it in turns to carry the basket, as they went scampering and cheeping and cackling in a long line behind.

Brother Mouse and Sister Mouse

Ruth Ainsworth

Once upon a time there were two little mice. They were brother and sister and they lived together on the beach in a bathing hut. This sounds a very odd place for two little mice to live, but they really were quite comfortable. They had a snug hole in a corner, between two boards. Whatever could they find to eat, living on the beach? Well, they couldn't eat fishy, salty things like seaweed and shrimps, because mice don't care for fishy, salty tastes. They ate delicious crumbs of cakes and biscuits and sandwiches.

Wherever did they find these delicious crumbs? They were dropped by the children and the grown-ups who used the bathing hut to undress in before they had a bathe, and to dress in afterwards. When the children came running and laughing and shivering up from the sea, their mothers nearly always said: "Here's a nice currant bun, dear, to eat while you are getting dressed." Or: "Here is a sandwich" – or "a biscuit" – or "a square of chocolate." The children always dropped crumbs as they ate and the little mice ran out of their hole, when no one was looking, and gobbled them up.

All through the summer the little mice kept fat and contented with their meals of crumbs, but when the summer was over, the children went back to their homes. It was much too cold to bathe, so the man who owned the bathing hut locked it up for the winter and went away too.

Poor little mice, how cold and hungry they felt. They crept over the pebbles and sand and tried to nibble bits

of seaweed but it was so nasty that they had to spit it out. One day, Brother Mouse found half a coconut at the edge of the sea. It was round and brown, rather like a basin.

"I have an idea," said Brother Mouse. "Find me two straight pieces of wood, Sister, about the same size."

Sister Mouse hunted here and there and found two strong, straight sticks. Then Brother Mouse jumped inside the half-coconut and took a stick in each paw and said: "Look Sister! This is our boat, and these can be oars to row with. Jump in beside me and let's go for a sail. We may find somewhere else to live in a place across the sea."

Sister Mouse was very frightened, but she did not want to be left behind, so she jumped in beside Brother Mouse. Just then a big wave came rushing in – *whoosh, whoosh* – and in a moment the little round boat was afloat. Oh, how the boat rolled and tossed, up – up – up – on one wave. Then down – down – down – on the next.

UP – d-o-o-w-n! UP – d-o-o-w-n! UP – d-o-o-w-n!

Sister Mouse began to feel sick, but Brother Mouse was too busy with the wooden oars to think of anything else. Soon they got used to being rolled and tossed about, and began to enjoy themselves. They could see nothing but blue sky above and green waves all round with foamy white tops.

They floated on for a very long time and they began to wonder if they ever *would* reach land. Their legs were stiff with sitting still so long, and Brother Mouse's arms ached with tugging at the wooden oars. Suddenly they saw something tall sticking up out of the water. "Land ahead!" shouted Brother Mouse. "Land ahead!"

Then the boat bumped into the tall thing and stopped moving. The tall thing was a huge wooden post. "Let's climb up the post and stretch our legs," said Sister Mouse. So they climbed up and up and up and up the post.

It was slippery with wet green seaweed, and prickly with ıarp, pointed shells. But at last they reached the top and ıere they found a wooden floor to walk about on.

Then suddenly they smelt a wonderful smell! It was a ıixture of toast and coffee and sausages and cake.

"Oh!" sighed Sister Mouse. "What a lovely smell!"

"Oh!" sighed Brother Mouse. "I am hungry!"

The two little mice scampered towards a doorway and ıe smell got stronger and stronger. The door was open, ɔ they crept in and saw they were in a café. No one was bout so they soon found a comfortable home in a hole in dark corner.

The café made a very good home. It was built on the ier and was open all the year round, winter and summer, nd there was always plenty of food and plenty of crumbs.)nce, someone said to the café lady: "I saw a mouse under ıe table. You must buy a mouse-trap and catch him." ut the lady said: "Mice? What an idea? Whoever heard f mice living at the end of a pier?" When Brother Mouse nd Sister Mouse heard that they hugged each other in ıeir safe little corner and felt glad they had left the cold athing hut on the beach and floated in their coconut boat ɔ this lovely, comfortable place.

ublished in *Listen with Mother Tales* (William Heinemann Ltd).

Dustman Pie

Mary Cockett

Jonathan was two years old and he was always very busy about everything. Every morning when it was fine he ran out of the house straight after breakfast to play in his sandpit.

His father had made it for him in the garden. He dug with his spade and filled little tins with sand and stood them along the edge of the sandpit. Then he emptied them out again. He had a little bucket too, for making sand pies, but he wasn't old enough to make very good pies.

Sometimes his mother and his sister made pies for him, and then he laughed and had a lovely time knocking them down. Now the morning I'm going to tell you about was a Monday morning, and Monday was the day when the dustman came and took away all the rubbish in the dustbin.

Jonathan liked the dustman. He was a big man, and he always smiled at Jonathan and spoke to him. Jonathan thought he was very clever to be able to lift the heavy dustbin on to his back and carry it away down the path.

Well, on this Monday morning when he brought the dustbin back empty, he tipped his cap back on his head and said to Johnathan: "Hello, making sand pies?"

"Yes," said Jonathan.

"Shall I make you a pie?" said the dustman.

"Lots of pies," said Jonathan.

"Oo, I can't make lots," said the dustman. "I have to get on with my work, you know. I'll make you just one."

Jonathan gave him the spade and the dustman bent

down by the sandpit, and filled the little bucket and patted the sand down hard. Then right in the corner of the sandpit he turned the bucket upside down and gently lifted it off. There, underneath, was a fine, tidy sand pie. "There you are, old son," said the dustman. "You make some more like that. I must be off now. Goodbye."

"Goodbye, dustman," said Jonathan, and he smiled all over his face. Then he ran into the house shouting: "Mummy, look, look, dustman pie!"

And his mother went outside and looked. "You lucky boy!" she said. "I've never known a dustman who made sand pies before."

And every time anybody called at the house that day, Jonathan said: "Come. Look. Dustman pie." They all looked and not one of them had ever seen a sand pie made by a dustman before.

I told you that Jonathan always knocked sand pies down, didn't I? But he didn't knock the dustman's pie down. And before he got into his bed that night he looked through his bedroom window down on to the sandpit. And there, right in the corner, he could see the little sand pie. "Goodnight, dustman pie!" shouted Jonathan. "Goodnight."

Supper Time

Herbert McKay

It was getting near supper-time, and Jim's dog barked: *Bow-wow!*

"Be quiet," cried Jim.

"How," said the dog, "how can I be quiet?"

"Well, what do you want?" asked Jim.

"Now," said the dog. "Now, now, I want my supper. Row, row! That's why I make a row, row!"

The cat mewed: *Mew, mew.*

"Be quiet," said Jim.

"I knew," said the cat, "I knew you would want me to be quiet."

"Well, what else do you want?" said Jim.

"A few – a few bits of fish and some milk," said the cat. "That's all I ask you to get me."

The donkey brayed: *He-haw, he-haw!*

"Be quiet," cried Jim.

"He saw," said the donkey. "It was the horse, and he saw."

"What was it he saw?" asked Jim.

"He saw," said the donkey, "he saw a load of hay and he did not give me any."

"Nay," said the horse. "I did not see a load of hay."

"What did you see then?" asked Jim.

"Hay," said the horse, "I certainly saw some hay. There was only a little so I ate it up."

The cow mooed: *Moo, moo.*

"Be quiet," said Jim.

"Do," said the cow.

"What do you want me to do?" asked Jim.

"Do," said the cow, "do give me some grass to chew, chew."

The pig squealed: *Eee-eee.*

"Be quiet," cried Jim.

"I feel," said the pig.

"What do you feel?" asked Jim.

"I feel," said the pig, "I feel as if I must squeal, squeal, squeal. I want a meal, meal, meal."

The owl hooted: *Hoo-hoo.*

"Be quiet," cried Jim.

"Who, who?" said the owl.

"Who what?" said Jim.

"Who, who," said the owl, "who, who would like to give me a mouse for my supper? Who, who?"

The mouse squeaked: *Week, week.*

"Weak," squeaked the mouse. "Weak, weak, I am far too weak, weak, to fight the owl. Too weak, weak. That's what I am." And the mouse ran down into its hole out of sight.

All the animals called out together, making a dreadful noise!

Bow-wow!
Mew, mew!
He-haw!
Moo-oo, moo-oo!
Eee-eee!
Hoo-hoo!
Week, week!

"All right," said Jim. "Be quiet and I'll get your suppers *now.*"

And he did.

Timothy's Bed

Christine Chaundler

Timothy was a boy who liked taking things to bed. His sister, Tabitha, liked taking things to bed with her, too, but she was sensible and only took one thing at a time.

But Timothy wasn't sensible. He liked to take all his toys to bed with him all at once, every night: a golliwog and a teddy-bear, a clockwork engine and a china dog, his garden spade and a box of paints, a jig-saw puzzle, a furry mouse, a boat, an elephant, a bat and a ball, and lots and lots of tin soldiers, Noah's Ark animals, and little things of that kind.

"If you take so many things to bed there won't be room for you," said Timothy's mother; and sometimes she took some of the bigger things out and put them on the floor beside the bed. Timothy was always very unhappy when his mother did this.

"They'll catch cold if they are left outside," he said.

Now Timothy and Tabitha were twins – so they were the same age. On their birthday when their father came home from work he brought two parcels with him. One was for Timothy, one for Tabitha. Inside Tabitha's parcel was a beautiful baby doll, and inside Timothy's was a splendid wooden horse on wheels, big enough for Timothy to sit on and to push along with his feet. Timothy and Tabitha were very pleased with their presents. They played with them all the evening, and when bedtime came they both took their new toys up to bed.

It was all right for Tabitha. It was the pink furry rabbit's turn to sleep with her that night, but there was plenty of room in her bed for the new doll as well. But it wasn't all right for Timothy. For a wooden horse on wheels is a very uncomfortable thing to have in bed with you. And remember, there was the golliwog and the teddy-bear, the clockwork engine and the china dog, the garden spade, the box of paints, the jig-saw puzzle, the boat, the mouse, the elephant, the bat and ball, the tin soldiers and the Noah's Ark animals as well.

"No, Timothy," said his mother, "you simply cannot take the wooden horse to bed with you! He can stand here, close beside the bed, where he can see you, and you can put out your hand and pat his head if you want to."

"Oh Mummy, can't I?" said Timothy.

"No – you cannot have him in bed," said Mother. "Now be a good boy and shut your eyes and go to sleep quickly, and when you wake up in the morning you can play with your horse again."

But Timothy *couldn't* go to sleep. He kept worrying and worrying about the new horse.

"He may be frightened at being in a new place," he thought. "And he's sure to be lonely and cold."

He put out his hand and stroked the horse's head. It did feel rather cold. Then suddenly Timothy felt he couldn't leave his poor horse outside any longer. He got out and picked up the horse and put it in the middle of his bed. Then he climbed back again. He had to lie on the very edge of the mattress, but there was just room for all the toys and himself, if he lay very, very straight and still. After a while Timothy fell asleep. And when he was asleep he didn't lie so still and straight. He rolled up into a ball, and – what do you think happened? Can you guess? He rolled right over the edge of the bed and fell down: *bump* onto the hard floor. Just like Humpty-dumpty!

Well, of course, that woke him up and he cried out

because he had bumped his head and he was so sleepy he couldn't think what had happened. His mother and father came running upstairs to see what was the matter.

Then Tabitha woke up and began to cry, too, because she was frightened at all the noise. And she and Timothy had to be kissed and comforted and given drinks of water and tucked up in bed again. And Timothy's mother took the horse and most of the the other things out of Timothy's bed and carried them away with her, right out of the room.

The next night, when bedtime came, Timothy's mother said: "Timothy, you really cannot take so many things to bed. You must choose just one *small* toy to have in bed with you, and the new horse and all the other things will have to stay outside."

"Oh, but they will catch the most dreadful colds and be so lonely and unhappy," cried Timothy.

"Oh, no, they won't!" said his mother. "I've put a big armchair close beside your bed, and here's the old shawl Tabitha used to wear when she was a baby. When you have chosen the toy that you would like to have in bed with you, you can put all the others on the armchair and cover them up with the shawl. And they will be quite warm and not at all lonely, and then you will have plenty of room in bed."

"All right," said Timothy. So he chose one toy to have in bed with him, then he put the new horse with the other toys in the big armchair and covered them up carefully with the warm old shawl. So everyone was happy and Timothy found that it was much more comfortable to have more room to himself in his bed.

The Two Little Men and the Toad and Billy Wind

Andrew Wilkinson

There were once two little men and a toad who lived in a cottage down a lane. Outside the cottage door there was hung a big, shining, brass door-bell.

One dark night, the two little men were sitting by the fire reading their newspapers, and the toad was sitting on the hearth, when the brass door-bell rang. The two little men went to the door, and opened it, and looked out.

"There's nobody there," said one little man.

"Nobody there," said the other little man.

So they closed the door and sat down by the fire again. And the toad, who was sitting on the hearth, chuckled to himself: "Keh-keh-keh!"

After a little while, the brass door-bell rang again. The two little men rushed to the door and opened it.

"There's nobody there," said one little man.

"Nobody there," said the other little man.

And they closed the door and went back to their chairs, feeling rather cross. But the toad began to laugh loudly: "Keh-keh-keh!"

"What's the matter, Toad?" asked one little man.

"Why," said the toad, "it's Billy Wind ringing your bell."

"Billy Wind!" said the other little man. "He can't do that! We'll catch him."

So they went to fetch a thick rope. And the next time the brass door-bell rang, the two little men rushed out into the dark and tied the rope round where they thought

Billy Wind was, and pulled it inside. But when they got inside where it was light, they found they hadn't caught anybody at all!

The toad chuckled. "Keh-keh! A rope's no good," he said.

So the two little men went to fetch a big chain. And next time the brass door-bell rang, they rushed out into the dark and fastened the chain round where they thought Billy Wind was, and pulled it inside. But when they got inside where it was light, they found they hadn't caught anybody at all!

And the toad laughed: "Keh-keh! A chain's no use," he said. "Try a sack."

So they went to fetch a big sack. And the next time the brass door-bell rang, the two little men rushed out into the dark and put the sack over where they thought Billy Wind was, and tied the neck tightly, and brought it inside. And this time they really *had* caught him! The sack jumped and bounced, and turned and wriggled on the floor, and from inside it there came a puffing and blowing noise, which gradually stopped, as though Billy Wind had got tired.

"We've got him," said the two little men. "He won't ring our brass door-bell and run away now."
And they sat by their fire and read their newspapers again. And nobody rang the bell outside.

But then, one little man said: "I've never seen Billy Wind."

"Neither have I," said the other. "I wonder what he looks like."

"Let's just open the sack a little and get a peep at him," said one.

"We won't let him get out," said the other, "just a peep."

So they opened the sack just a little, and as they did so there was a gentle whistling noise. "Phew-phew-phew," it went, "phew-phew-phew."

"I can't see him," said one.

"Neither can I," said the other. And they opened the sack wider. But no Billy Wind could they find.

For when they had first opened the sack, Billy Wind had slipped out, "phew-w-w," and under the door, "phew-w-w," and out into the darkness, "phew-w-w."

"Where's he gone?" asked one little man, very surprised.

"You'll soon find out," said the toad, laughing fit to burst. "Keh-keh-keh! Just you listen!"

They listened. And, sure enough, they heard Billy Wind. He was ringing their brass door-bell for all he was worth, as though he would never stop.

Ring-a-ring-a-ring-a-ring!

ʼThe Sea and the Sandcastle

ᴾenelope Pine

ʼlartin was very little. He was only one year old. He could ·ot walk yet, but he could crawl very well indeed. He had little, tiny, rubber spade and a little, tiny, rubber bucket nd he sat, all alone, in the middle of the great big beach.

Every now and then Martin scooped up a little sand n his tiny spade and dropped it over his shoulder. Ie was trying to make a sand-castle, but he wasn't very ood at it. Still, he enjoyed himself a great deal and he hattered away to himself, and to the seagulls who flew over ɔ watch him, and to the far-away sea, that whispered at he edge of the beach. "Swish-swish, swish-swish," it said.

Presently a little girl came running down the beach. Ier name was Nicola.

"Hello, Martin! I'm going to help you," she called, nd began to pile sand on his tiny castle with her wooden pade.

"Na, na, na," Martin screamed and waved his spade at er, for he wanted to build his castle in his own way. ʼut Nicola was three and she had come specially to help er little brother, and help him she did. And when Martin aw how well Nicola could build castles he was glad she ad come to help him.

They had a very happy time sitting there in the middle f the big empty beach and talking to themselves and each ther and the seagulls, and building their little castles. ʌnd far away on the edge of the beach, but not quite so far way now, the sea was talking to itself, too. "Swish-swish, wish-swish," it whispered.

In a little while another girl came running down the beach. Her name was Alison and she was really quite a big girl, for she was six years old and she went to school. She was carrying an iron spade.

"Hello, you two, I'm going to help you build a big castle!"

"No, this is our castle, no, no, *no*," squealed Nicola.

"Na, na, na," cried Martin.

But Alison was their big sister and she didn't take a bit of notice. She began to dig right away with her iron spade. When Nicola and Martin saw how fast the castle was growing they were glad that Alison had come to help them and they started to dig again, too.

They all talked to themselves and each other and had a very happy time. A seagull flew over and cried to his friend the sea: "They're getting on, they're building a castle!"

And, far away, but not so far away as before, the sea whispered and chuckled to itself as it lapped at the edge of the sand. "Swish-swish, swish-swish," it laughed to itself.

In a little while quite a big girl came running down the beach. Her name was Hilary and she was the oldest of the family. She had brought her large iron spade with her.

"Hello, you three, I've come to help you build a really big castle!" she shouted.

"No! This is our castle."

"You build your own!"

"Na, na, na!"

Alison, Nicola and Martin had been having a very good time together! But Hilary didn't take a bit of notice because she was their big sister. She just started to dig with her big spade and when the others saw how fast their castle was growing now that Hilary was helping them, they were

glad she had come. They all dug together as hard as they could, even Martin, though he took as much sand off the castle as he put on it.

The seagull flew over again. "They're making a very big castle now!" he called to his friend the sea. And the sea, which was much nearer now, whispered and chuckled to itself at the edge of the sand as it wiped out all the marks that the people had made since last it had washed the beach.

After a while a man came striding down the beach. He carried a great big shovel.

"Oh, Daddy!" laughed the children, excitedly, as he began to throw huge shovelfuls of sand on top of the castle, all except Martin who shrieked, "Na, na, na," at the top of his voice.

The castle grew faster and faster. They all dug and dug and dug, as hard as they could, even Martin.

Then the seagull flew over again. "Hurry up, old sea! They're making such a big castle that you'll never be able to wipe it out if you don't hurry up."

But this time the sea was very near indeed. He was rather surprised when he saw what an enormous castle that busy family had made. But he didn't worry. He just whispered and chuckled quietly to himself and sent his little waves lap, lap, lapping towards that castle, nearer, nearer, until, quite suddenly, an extra big wave swished right round the castle.

"No, no, no," they all cried together, "go and wash the beach somewhere else, old sea, this is our castle and we don't want it washed away."

But the sea didn't take a bit of notice. He was used to people and their castles. He just came swishing in, and in, quite gently, wave by wave, until he had made an island of that castle. Daddy had to pick up Martin and take him back to the beach hut. But the sea didn't stop. It came in, further and further, until it got too deep for Nicola and she had to go back to the hut, too.

But still the sea wouldn't stop. In and in it came until, at last, it got too deep for Alison. And then it got too deep for Hilary, and she had to go back to the hut. And in the end Daddy found that the sea was splashing his shorts, and he had to go in, too.

So there they all sat, in the hut, watching the sea coming

n, and in, and the castle getting smaller and smaller ıntil, at last, only the little flag that Daddy had stuck in he top was left above the water, and at last, even that loated away.

"Well it was a lovely castle," they all agreed, as they vent home to bed. And, next day, when the sea had gone ut again, the sand was just as flat as it had been before hey began to dig.

The sea was still laughing to itself, far away at the edge f the beach. "Swish-swish, swish-swish," it called. "You an make another castle," it seemed to say. "I've made he sand all flat and clean for you to make another one!"

And that's exactly what they did.

The Axle's Broken

Helen Christison

The motor-car was big and black and shiny, and it went up the road so fast that the axle broke with a crack!

And when the axle broke, the wheels began to squeak, and when the wheels began to squeak the tyres said: "Wheels, wheels, why do you squeak?"

"The axle's broken," said the wheels, "and so we squeak."

So the tyres said, "Then we'll go flat. *Pfff. Pffff!*"

And when the tyres did that, the mudguards said: "Tyres, why do you go flat?"

"The axle's broken," said the tyres, "and the wheels squeak, and so we go flat. *Pffff.*"

So the mudguards said: "Then we'll rattle."

And when the mudguards did that the headlamps said: "Mudguards, why do you rattle?"

"The axle's broken," said the mudguards, "and the wheels squeak, the tyres go flat, and so we rattle."

Then the headlamps said: "We'll blink," and so they went blinkety blink.

And when the headlamps did that the engine said: "Headlamps, why do you blink?"

"The axle's broken," said the headlamps, "and the wheels squeak, the tyres go flat, and the mudguards rattle, and so we blink."

So the engine said, "I'll stop."

And when the engine stopped the hooter said: "Engine, why do you stop?"

"The axle's broken," said the engine, "and the wheels

queak, the tyres go flat, the mudguards rattle, the head-
mps blink, and so I stop."
So the hooter said: "I'll hoot."
And when he did that the windscreen wiper said:
Hooter, why do you hoot?"
"The axle's broken," said the hooter, "and the wheels
queak, the tyres go flat, and the mudguards rattle, the
eadlamps blink, and the engine stops, and so I hoot."
So the windscreen wiper said: "I'll wibble-wobble."
o the windscreen wiper did wibble-wobble.
And when it did that the window said: "Windscreen
iper, why do you wibble-wobble?"
"The axle's broken," said the windscreen wiper, "and
ie wheels squeak, the tyres go flat, and the mudguards
attle, the headlamps blink, and the engine stops, the
ooter hoots and so I wibble-wobble."
So the window said: "I'll break."
And when the window did that the driver said:
Window, why do you break?"
"The axle's broken," said the window, "and the wheels
queak, the tyres go flat, and the mudguards rattle, the
eadlamps blink, and the engine stops, the hooter hoots,
ie windscreen wiper goes wibble-wobble, and so I break."
So the driver said: "I'll get out."
And when he got out the door said: "Driver, why do
ou get out?"
"The axle's broken," said the driver, "and the wheels
queak, the tyres go flat, and the mudguards rattle, the
eadlamps blink, and the engine stops, the hooter hoots,
ie windscreen wiper goes wibble-wobble, and the window
reaks, and so I get out."
So the door said: "I'll fall off."
And when the door fell off, the roof said: "Door, why
o you fall off?"

"The axle's broken," said the door, "and the wheels squeak, the tyres go flat, and the mudguards rattle, the headlamps blink, and the engine stops, the hooter hoots, the windscreen wiper goes wibble-wobble, and the window breaks, the driver gets out, and so I fall off."

So the roof said: "I'll fall in."

So the roof fell in, and the door fell off, the driver got out, and the window broke, the windscreen wiper went wibble-wobble, and the hooter hooted, the engine stopped and the headlamps blinked, the mudguards rattled, and the tyres went flat, the wheels squeaked, and the axle broke, and the driver had to go home by bus.

ig Fat Puss-Cat

heila Hayley

g Fat Puss-Cat lay sleeping on the wall in the garden in
e sun. She slept and slept.

Toby Dog came out into *his* garden next door. He ran
und and round, and chased his tail, and barked. Then
saw Big Fat Puss-Cat asleep on the wall.

"Hey you, Big Fat Puss-Cat," he said. "What are you
ing on that wall – you lazy old Big Fat Puss-Cat?"

Big Fat Puss-Cat opened one eye and looked down on
by Dog. "Why make all that fuss and bother?" she said.
am sleeping on this wall."

"Do you know," Toby Dog barked, "do you know,
u're the biggest, fattest Puss-Cat I ever saw."

"I *know* I'm a Big Fat Puss-Cat," she said, and she
iled and curled herself round. She tucked her furry tail
tween her front feet and over her big, fat nose and went
sleep again.

After a little while Wally Tortoise came slowly through
e grass and stopped in the cool shade of the wall where
g Fat Puss-Cat was sleeping. He looked up at the wall
d said: "Really, Big Fat Puss-Cat, must you sleep all
y? I remember when you were a tiny little kitten. You
ere as pretty as a picture. But now you are just Big Fat
ss-Cat because you sleep all day."

Big Fat Puss-Cat kept her eyes closed, but she said: "I
e being a Big Fat Puss-Cat, Wally Tortoise – I *like* it."
ie began to purr to herself, and soon she was aleep again.

After a little while Missis came out of the house to shake
e mats and said to herself: "Oh, *there's* that Big Fat

Puss-Cat of mine. Lazy old Puss-Cat." And she went on shaking her mats and the dust came flying out. Up and up into the air it went, and all over the garden it spread, and all over Big Fat Puss-Cat – suddenly Big Fat Puss-Cat sneezed: "ATISHOO!"

"Serves you right, Big Fat Puss-Cat," said Missis, and she laughed. "You're so fat and sleepy it will do you good to sneeze. Why haven't you chased that little mouse away?"

"Atishoo!" sneezed Big Fat Puss-Cat. "Atishoo!"

"You're too lazy – that's what it is," said Missis. "Every night that mouse *laughs* at you, Big Fat Puss-Cat, when it sees you asleep all the time."

Big Fat Puss-Cat sat up and blinked. "*I* never heard a mouse," she said.

"'Course you never heard a mouse," said Missis. "How can you hear anything when you sleep all the time?"

Big Fat Puss-Cat got down from the wall and walked away waving her tail in the air – she was thinking and making a plan.

That night Big Fat Puss-Cat lay in her basket under the kitchen table as usual. But she kept *awake*, all night – she only *pretended* to be asleep. Soon she heard a little noise – pit-pat, pit-pat, pit-pat, pit-pat. Puss-Cat opened one eye and saw the little mouse walking across the floor. So she shut her eye quickly.

The little mouse looked at Big Fat Puss-Cat and giggled. "Old Big Fat Puss-Cat's fast asleeep again," he said. "Lazy old Puss-Cat! Fat old Puss-Cat! Big old Puss-Cat!"

Big Fat Puss-Cat kept very still.

The little mouse walked away – pit-pat, pit-pat – humming to himself. But before he had gone very far Big Fat Puss-Cat got up, and arched her back and SPAT!

"Get out of my kitchen," she said. "Shoo, shoo, be off with you. Be off with you. Don't ever dare to come back again – or I'll *catch* you!"

The little mouse was so surprised that he slid right across the floor, banged against the wall – then picked himself up and went head-over-heels, head-over-heels down into his little hole, and never came into the kitchen again.

In the morning, when Missis came into the kitchen, she said: "Did that cheeky mouse come again?"

"Yes," said Big Fat Puss-Cat, "but he won't come again – I blew him across the kitchen and right down his hole."

"There's a good, clever Puss-Cat," said Missis. "You shall have a nice big dinner of liver today and fish tomorrow. You *are* a beautiful Big Fat Puss-Cat."

"I *like* being a Big Fat Puss-Cat," said Big Fat Puss-Cat, and she purred and purred and purred until she fell asleep.

Frank's Adventure

Dorothy Edwards

There was once a boy, and this boy's name was Frank, and one day, this boy, Frank, wanted to have an adventure. He wanted to go out into the wide world and do a really exciting thing. But he couldn't; and do you know why he couldn't?

Because it was RAINING. The fat cold raindrops were rattling on the trees, and dead wet leaves were dashing across the road, and it was cold, cold, COLD.

So the boy couldn't go out at all. His mother said: "Frank, you can't go out into the wide world today to have an adventure, it is too wet and blowy and cold."

So this boy Frank stayed indoors. But he thought and thought and soon he had a GOOD IDEA.

"I *will* have an adventure," this boy Frank said, "I'll have an adventure just the same."

So he put on his adventure hat, and his adventure coat, and his mother helped him to fasten his adventure belt and off he went. Because he was indoors he didn't wear his adventure boots. He wore his new red-rabbit bedroom-slippers.

So this boy Frank started his adventure. He set off from the kitchen where the pots and pans and the sink and the stove were, and where his mother was peeling potatoes for dinner, and he said: "Goodbye, Mother. I'm off."

But his mother said, "Wait a minute," and she took down the peg-bag from behind the kitchen door. She emptied out the pegs, and into the peg-bag she put four brown ginger biscuits and a bottle of cold white milk,

and she fastened the peg-bag on this boy Frank's back and said: "Goodbye, Frank. Have a good adventure."

So off he went.

He sat on a little old cushion and slowly, slowly he went down the passage from the kitchen door. He went slowly because he said it was a deep river, not a passage, and he only had a very small boat. (This small boat was the little old cushion, of course.)

Down the passage Frank went on his little bumping boat, past the open door of the dining-room. He said this room was an island. On this island Frank could see Tig the pussycat licking her furry black leg, and Bubble the goldfish going round and round in his glass bowl, and Peter the dog lying with his nose on the fender.

"Those are the island people," said Frank.

"Miaow-miaow, bobble-bubble, bobble-bubble, wow-wow," the island people said. "Come and visit us."

But Frank in his little bumping boat went on past the island.

And then he came to the sitting-room door, and that was shut and Frank said it was a big cliff that no one could climb. And then he came to the front door, and the inside of the letter-box was moving just a little bit because of the wind and the rain, and: "That's a friendly lady waving 'goodbye' to me," said Frank, and he called back to her, "Goodbye, I'm going to climb the mountain now," and he got out of his little bumping boat, and slowly, slowly, because it was so very steep, he began to climb the mountain. (And you know what the mountain was, don't you? Yes, the stairs!)

Up and up the mountain went this boy Frank. Up and up the white mountain stairs.

How that boy Frank panted and puffed! It *was* a steep high mountain! But he got to the top at last and then he sat down and looked all about him. There was the river, away below, and the friendly island, and the cliff he couldn't climb, and all the things he'd passed on his travels so far.

"I can see cows and sheep and houses and churches and cinemas and people," said this boy Frank, "what a very high mountain this is!"

Then he took off his mother's peg-bag and opened it, and took out his four ginger biscuits, and his bottle of milk, he took out a little peg, too, that had stayed in the bag by mistake. He ate the biscuits and drank the milk, for his long journey had made him hungry and thirsty.

"This little peg is magic," he said. "It will take me to a very magic place."

Then this boy Frank got up, and he took his magic peg, and along the landing he went, marching, marching like a soldier now, holding the magic peg in front of him. Left

ght, left right. Past a door and past a door and past a
or he went all among the high mountains.
Then he came to a door that was open just a crack.
"This is a rather secret and *dangerous* place," said that
y Frank. "But because I have a magic peg, I can wriggle
rough."
And he did. He wriggled through without opening the
or any more, very carefully, very wriggly. And when he
t through he was in his very own *bedroom*. There was his
d and his chair and his box and his teddy bear and all
s toys.
"This is a fine place," said he, "this is a very fine place
r a boy to live in."
And he took off his adventure hat, and his adventure
lt and coat and his red-rabbit slippers, and he climbed
to his own comfortable bed.
"Here I am," he called out to his mother. "Here I am at
st, in a nice little house on the top of the mountain,
ter my adventure. I shall stay here, Mother, until it is
nner-time."
"All right," called Mother. "I'll call you when it's
ady."

Three Jolly Sailormen
Ursula Hourihane

There were once three jolly sailormen.

The first one, Sailor Bill, could never sit still.

The second one, Sailor Dick, was as thin as a stick.

The third one, Sailor Joe, was as round as an o.

These three jolly sailormen were the best of friends and they sailed the seven seas in the *Betsy May*. That was the name of their ship.

One day Sailor Joe (who was round as an o) said to his friends: "D'you know what I've been thinking? I think it's time we three jolly sailormen settled down on shore."

Well! The other two sailormen were so surprised they could hardly speak.

"Settle down on shore, did you say?" cried Sailor Dick (thin as a stick).

"Settle down on shore, did you say?" echoed Sailor Bill (who could never sit still).

Then they both said together: "Whatever made you think that, Sailor Joe?"

Sailor Joe's round face looked very solemn. "We've sailed all up and down the seven seas," he said. "We've sailed all round the world. We've seen all the sights and wonders everywhere but – we've never had a *home*, have we? And I think it's time we had a nice snug little home of our own somewhere."

Sailor Dick and Sailor Bill looked very solemn and thought hard and then they said: "You're quite right, Sailor Joe. We've never had a home. It's quite time we had a snug little home of our own."

So the three jolly sailormen sat in the sun on the deck
the *Betsy May* and planned where they would have their
me.
"It must be somewhere where the sun shines and the
ies are blue," said Sailor Joe (round as an o).
"It must be somewhere where we can make a little
rden and grow fruit and vegetables and flowers," said
ilor Bill (who could never sit still).
"What about that little island with the monkeys?" said
ilor Dick (thin as a stick).
"The one with the parrots and tortoises?" said Sailor
e.
"The one where the birds are bright as tiny rainbows
d the fish are red and orange and green?" said Sailor
ill.
"Yes," said Sailor Dick, "that's the one I mean."
And then they all said together: "That's where we'll
ake our home."
So they hoisted the sails of the *Betsy May* and away they
ent to find their island. They sailed on and on for three
ays and three nights while a gentle breeze puffed out the
ils. Then one night the gentle breeze began to blow
arder and harder till it turned into a regular gale. All
ight long the storm blew and blew and the three jolly
ilormen began to wonder if they would ever reach their
land.
But when the morning came the wind grew tired of
owing and storming and went away and the sea grew
lm and blue again.
Sailor Dick was just busy dishing up the stew for dinner
hen he heard Sailor Joe shout: "Land ahoy! The island!
he island! I can see the island!"
Sailor Dick rushed up on deck to see.
Sailor Bill heard Sailor Joe's cry too, and raced up on

deck to see the island. There it was, across the blue water, with its sands shining golden and bright in the sunlight.

"Hurrah for the island! Hurrah for our new home!" cried the three jolly sailormen.

It didn't take the *Betsy May* very long to sail over the water and slide gently up on to the sands. They tied her up safely to a palm tree and then looked round for a place to build their home. Of course they hadn't any bricks but they soon found plenty of good logs and branches, and in next to no time they had built a fine little house. Then they sat round their camp fire and had their tea.

"Chee-chee-chee!" Suddenly a strange little voice chattered behind Sailor Bill.

He turned round with a piece of cake in his hand to see who was there. What do you think? A little brown monkey snatched the cake out of his hand and ran up on to his shoulder.

"Well, I never did!" laughed Sailor Bill. "You want to come and live with me, do you Jacko? All right, you shall."

And ever after that the little brown monkey was Sailor Bill's own special pet.

"Squawk! Squawk!" Then a strange voice screeched behind Sailor Dick. Sailor Dick was just going to put a lump of sugar in his tea, but he turned round, and what do you think? An old grey parrot snatched the lump of sugar out of his hand and perched on his head!

"Well, I never did!" laughed Sailor Dick. "You want to come and live with me, do you, Polly? All right, you shall." And ever after that the old grey parrot was Sailor Dick's own special pet.

"Hi! What's this pushing into me?" cried Sailor Joe. And what do you think? A slow and solid tortoise was poking his wrinkled little head into Sailor Joe's pocket.

"Well, I never did!" laughed Sailor Joe. "You want to come and live with me, do you, Tommy Tortoise? All right, so you shall!" And ever after that the slow solid tortoise was Sailor Joe's own special pet.

And there live the three jolly sailormen – Sailor Bill (who could never sit still), Sailor Dick (thin as a stick) and Sailor Joe (round as an o); with the monkey, the parrot and the slow solid tortoise. I wish I could see them, don't you?

Teddy Goes Camping
Diana Ross

William had decided to be difficult.

Some friends had lent Father a tent, and he had taken William's older brother and sister camping for the week-end. But they didn't take William.

As soon as they were gone, William said: "But *why* can't I go, Mummy?"

"We've told you, William," said Mother. "The tent will only take three, and you really are rather too young yet."

"You could get another tent, and I'm not too young," said William.

"You have your treats, and the big ones have their treats."

"I don't like my treats," said William.

"William," said Mother, "decide what you want to do and go and do it. I'll count three. One – "

When Mother counted three the children knew that she meant it.

"I'll play in the garden. But I won't *like* it," said William gloomily. And off he went looking very sulky indeed.

But as he went by the rubbish bin he saw an old groundsheet which Father had thrown out when they were packing for the camp. It had a hole in one corner, but most of it seemed quite good to William. He pulled it out and looked at it, and then he had an idea.

"Mummy, Mummy," he cried, running back into the kitchen. "Can I have this old groundsheet? Can I cut it up?"

"Yes, William," said Mother. "You can do what you like with it. What is it for?"

"I'll show you when it's done," said William.

Off he ran, and Mother smiled to see him so busy – then she went upstairs to do the beds. She had just begun to make William's when she heard him rushing upstairs.

"Are you ready? Shall I come?" asked Mother.

"No, not yet. I want Teddy," said William.

Mother dug Teddy out from the bottom of the bed and turned his head round so that it faced his toes.

"Thank you," said William. "Can you find him his kilt and his red jersey?"

"Oh! Is Teddy going visiting?" asked Mother.

"No," said William. "But he will need to be warm."

Mother felt down inside William's bed again. "Here is the jersey," she said, "and here is the kilt – Teddy seems to be a restless sleeper. His clothes get all over the place."

"Thank you," said William, and rushed off with Teddy and his clothes. Mother finished the beds and the washing up and then she heard William calling. "Come now, Mummy. It's ready. Mummy, come now."

Mother went down to the very farthest end of the garden to a sheltered place the children called the grove. And there she saw, on the grass, a little tent made out of a bit of the old groundsheet, with Teddy sitting beside it. She knelt down and looked inside. On the ground was another piece of groundsheet cut to the right size, and a folded blanket from the doll's cot lay upon it.

"William, it's wonderful," she said. "It's exactly like a real one! What makes it stay up?"

"Two drumsticks," said William. "I found them in the playbox."

"I'm sure Teddy will love camping out in this little tent," said Mother.

"He ought to have a sleeping bag," said William, "like the ones you made out of blanket for Caroline and Johnny. Could I sew this doll's blanket up and make it like a real one for him?"

"Of course you shall," said Mother. "Is Teddy going to sleep here tonight?"

"Yes," said William. "He asked if he could and I said 'yes'. But I want to make him a proper bag to sleep in."

"And quite right too," said Mother.

So they took the doll's blanket and went in and found a needle and some red wool, and Mother showed William how to sew the sides together.

"I must go and get the dinner," said Mother, when William had finished his sewing.

"Can't we have dinner in camp?" asked William.

"I don't see why not," said Mother. "I haven't begun to cook it yet. We can have a proper camp dinner."

She boiled eggs and washed lettuce and opened a tin of meat and cut bread and butter and they took it all in a basket to the grove and ate it there.

"Couldn't we have a camp fire? Daddy said he and Caroline and Johnny are going to."

"You can have one tonight," said Mother, "before you go to bed. I haven't time to help you with it now. I've got some people coming to see me."

So William played camping all the afternoon, and had his tea there too, alone with Teddy, and after that he prepared the camp fire. He found two flat stones and put them near each other, and in the space between he put scraps of paper and some dry grass and tiny twigs. By the side of the fire he made a pile of bigger twigs and sticks, because this is what he had seen Johnny do when he had been practising making a camp fire. Then he ran in and

got the doll's saucepan and filled it with water – and then he went and found Mother.

"The camp fire is all ready," he said. "Can we light it now?"

"Wait till I get the matches," said Mother.

When Mother saw how carefully William had made the camp fire she said: "But this is splendid, William! It looks as if we won't have any trouble with this fire." And sure enough, as soon as Mother put a lighted match to the paper it caught fire and then the sticks began to crackle.

"Very good," said Mother. "I couldn't have made a better fire myself." William had never felt so proud. He watched his fire, and when it was going really well, he put the doll's saucepan (which was full of water) on the flat stones over the fire and poked wisps of grass and tiny twigs into the flame under it until the water boiled. Then he put a quarter of a meat cube into it and made real soup. Then with doll's spoons, he and Mother ate from the saucepan turn and turn about.

"It's really Teddy's supper," said William. "But I have to eat it for him."

"Of course," said Mother. "I think he's enjoying it as much as we are."

As soon as the soup was finished Teddy was undressed and put in his sleeping bag. His clothes were folded up and put under his head for a pillow, and there he lay inside the little tent like a real camper.

"Will you leave the end open?" asked Mother.

"No, because it might rain," said William. And he shut the little opening and Mother gave him a pin to fasten it, in case the wind came and blew it open during the night.

"Goodnight, Teddy," said William.

"Sleep well," said Mother.

But Teddy didn't answer, so perhaps he had already

fallen asleep. Well, it did rain in the night. It rained and it rained and it rained. William woke up and heard it, and wondered how Teddy was getting on out there in the darkness of his little tent.

It was fine next morning, and before breakfast William ran down through the wet grass to see how Teddy was. When he opened the flap at the end of the little tent, there lay Teddy just as he had left him, as dry and comfortable as could be. But at his side: wonder of wonders! There was something on the ground. It was a little rucksack just the size for a Teddy! It was made of green waterproof, with an outside pocket, and shoulder straps of braid.

"Oh," said William. He picked it up and opened it. It was full of dolly mixture sweets – just what a Teddy would want to take camping.

"Oh," said William again. Then he picked up Teddy and rushed into the house and up to Mother's bedroom.

"Mummy! Mummy! Look! Look what I found! Teddy's got a rucksack. Oh, Mummy, where did it come from?"

"Well, you don't suppose such an experienced camper as Teddy would go camping without a rucksack, do you?" said Mother, laughing.

"You made it last night. You *must* have made it."

"You'd better ask Teddy," said Mother.

Well, next day, when Father and Caroline and Johnny came home and told Mother and William all about their camping, William said: "Teddy camped. He's camping still, and he's got a rucksack. Come and see him."

So William led them all down the garden to the grove to inspect Teddy's camp. Father said it was just as good as theirs, and William asked Father and Caroline and Johnny to come and have supper with him and Teddy.

The Elephant and the Little Boy

Harold J. Harland

There was once an elephant who lived in a zoo. One night this elephant could *not* go to sleep, although he tried and tried, so he thought he would get up and go for a walk. Round and round the zoo he went and, as it was in the middle of the night, there was no one about and no one for him to talk to. When he came to the gate he found that someone had left it open.

"Oh!" thought the elephant. "The gate is open! I will go for a walk round the town." So through the gate he went and along the street. *Thump, thump, thumpety, thump, thump, thump, thumpety, thump.*

On and on he went until he came to some crossroads. One road went to the left, one road went to the right, and one road went straight on.

The elephant turned to the left, but he should have turned to the right to get back to the zoo. A little farther on he came to some more crossroads. One road went to the left, one road went to the right, and one road went straight on.

"Oh," thought the elephant, "where shall I go now?" And this time he turned to the right when he should have turned to the left. On he walked going up this road and down that until the morning came and it was light again.

"Well, I don't know where the zoo is," thought the elephant, "big as I am, I have got lost."

Then he saw a milkman coming along carrying a wire basket full of bottles of milk. But when the milkman saw the elephant he was so frightened that he dropped his basket

full of milk bottles and ran away as fast as his legs would go.

Then a postman came along with a lot of letters. Suddenly he saw the elephant and he was so frightened that he dropped all his letters in the middle of the road and ran away as fast as he could go.

"Well," thought the elephant, "nobody seems to want to talk to me this morning," so he turned into the next street and there he saw a man putting newspapers through letter-boxes.

Well, when this man turned round and saw the elephant looking at him, he was so frightened he ran up a narrow passage between two houses and hid there, because he knew the elephant was far too big to follow him into such a narrow place.

"Everybody seems frightened of me," thought the elephant, "whatever shall I do?"

Then a little boy came running out of a house. "Oh, what a lovely big elephant," said the little boy. "Are you all by yourself?"

"Yes," said the elephant, "what is your name, little boy?"

"My name is Brian," said the little boy.

"Can you show me the way back to the zoo?" said the elephant.

"Oh yes," said the little boy, "I will take you there if you like."

"Oh thank you," said the elephant. "Would you like to ride on my back?"

"Yes please," said the little boy. So the elephant crouched down in the road and the little boy climbed up on his back. Then the elephant got up very carefully – his back was so broad that the little boy felt quite safe sitting there. Along the road they went, and when the little boy wanted the elephant to turn to the left he patted him on the left ear, and when he wanted the elephant to turn to the right he patted him on the right ear. So they went on until they came to the zoo.

The man who looked after the elephant was standing at the gate. He could hardly believe his eyes when he saw the little boy guiding the elephant so cleverly. He opened the gate wide, and the elephant walked through. Then he crouched down on the ground again and the little boy jumped off.

The keeper shook hands with the little boy and said: "Thank you very much indeed. Come back any time you like with your father and mother and I'll be pleased to show you all over the zoo and tell you anything you want to know about our animals."

"Thank you," said the little boy, "I'd like to come often."

By this time the elephant was standing up again. His great trunk was swaying from side to side and his little eyes were smiling.

"Goodbye, little boy," he said. "Thank you for bringing me home when I was lost."

"Goodbye," said the little boy. "I'll see you when I come back with my mummy and daddy and then perhaps you will give me another ride on your back."

"Indeed I will," said the elephant.

Then the little boy went home feeling very pleased with himself.

’enny, Tuppence and Joey t the Fishmarket

Aary Walker

he triplets, Penny, Tuppence and Joey, lived in a aside town, and every Thursday afternoon their randmother came to look after them. Penny, Tuppence ıd Joey looked forward to Thursday afternoons, for anny – that's what they called their grandmother – ways had something new to show them.

One day she said: "How would you like to go to the ishmarket today? If we hurry we can get there just as the ›ats come in and unload all the fish."

"Oh! How lovely!" cried the triplets. "We've never been the Fishmarket before!"

"All right then, get your coats and hats and put your oolly scarves on," said Nanny. "It will be a bit blowy ›wn at the harbour."

The children wasted no time getting ready, and soon ıey were all hurrying to the end of the road to catch the g red double-decker bus.

"Can we go upstairs on the bus?" asked Joey. I like sitting upstairs at the very front, then I can see erything!"

"Yes," said Nanny, "so do I." They were lucky, for the vo front seats upstairs on the bus were empty, so Joey and enny sat on one side of the gangway, and Nanny and uppence on the other side.

"Ding, ding," went the bell, and away went the bus. ›on the conductor came upstairs, calling, "Fares, please!"

and Nanny said, "One and three halves to the harbour, please."

"We're going to the Fishmarket," said Joey to the conductor. "Have you ever been to the Fishmarket?"

"Oh, lots of times," laughed the conductor, "it's fun! Mind a crab doesn't catch your finger though!" and he went off down the stairs again.

When the bus reached the harbour Nanny and the triplets got off. "Goodbye," said the conductor. "And don forget what I said about the crabs, sonny!"

"*Will* a crab pinch my finger, Nanny?" asked Joey.

"Well, that's up to you," said Nanny. "If you don't touch *them*, they won't pinch *you!*"

"Well, I'll keep my hands in my pockets," said Joey, "then they can't, can they?"

Soon they arrived at the quayside where the fishing boa were. Lots of men in thick, dark-blue jerseys and high rubber boots were lifting the heavy baskets of fish out of the boats and up on to the quay. These baskets were taken to a big open shed, and fish were poured out on to the raise floor in big shining silvery heaps. There were all sorts of fish: soles and plaice and cod and haddock, all wet and shiny in the afternoon sun.

"Oh Nanny," said Tuppence, "I don't like the smell! I think it's nasty!"

But Joey said, "I like it! It smells a bit like seaweed. Where are the crabs, Nanny? I want to see the crabs!"

But just then Tuppence suddenly called out, "Oh, look! Did you see that tabby cat? He came around the corner ever so quickly and stole a fish – look! there he goes!" And sure enough there *was* the tabby cat streaking along the quayside with a whole fish in his mouth.

"Oh! Poor little cat," said Penny. "I expect he was hungry. He's ever so thin."

"I shouldn't be surprised if he comes back for another fish soon," said Nanny. "We'll watch out for him."

Just then one of the fishermen came up with another basket and emptied it on to the floor and out poured dozens of crabs, all alive!

"There you are, Joey," said Nanny, "crabs – just look at them!" Joey pushed his hands right down into the pockets of his coat as he watched them walking about the floor.

"Oh, look, Nanny," he shouted, "they walk sideways! Can't they walk straight?"

"Crabs always walk sideways," Nanny said.

"I can do that!" cried Joey, and he started to walk sideways across the quay, but he bumped right into a man who was carrying another basket to the shed. Joey grabbed at the basket to steady himself, and then, "Ow! Ow!" he shrieked! It was another basket of crabs, and a big one right on top had pinched Joey's finger in its claws.

"That'll teach you to go crab-walking, young man!" laughed the fisherman as he pulled the crab's claws away. "Did he hurt you?"

"Well, I had my glove on so it didn't really hurt very much," said Joey, and he ran back to Nanny.

"Nanny! Nanny!" he cried. "A crab pinched my finger! Look!"

But Nanny and Tuppence and Penny were too busy watching the tabby cat who had come back and was hiding behind the shed. He kept poking his head round the orner, then darting back again, but suddenly he dashed ut like a streak of lightning, grabbed another fish in is mouth, and raced off again down the quay.

One of the fishermen saw him, but he only laughed and said to the children, "He comes every day and steals a couple of fish. He's a bit wild and won't be friendly with us.

If we offer him a fish he runs away – he likes to come and get his own!"

"Are all the boats unloaded now?" Penny asked him.

"Yes," he said, "and here come the fishmongers to buy the fish."

"Oh, dear!" said Nanny. "I was hoping I might buy some plaice to take home for tea, but I suppose it will all be sold in big lots."

"Oh, you can buy a *few* plaice if you like," said the fisherman. "Here, how about these?" And he picked up four big plump plaice.

"Oh, lovely!" said Nanny, as she paid him for them, and he wrapped them up in plenty of newspaper. "Now come on, children."

"Let's look for the tabby cat," said Penny. "He must be along here somewhere." Presently they saw him perched on a ledge of the sea-wall just above the water, washing his face with his paws and looking *so* contented.

"*He's* had a *very* good tea!" said Nanny, "and now I think we must catch the bus and go home with the fish for *our* tea."

ꟳun with Willy Wind

Winifred Doran

Villy Wind woke up one fine morning and shouted appily:

"Oh! ho! hee! hee! I see Mr Sun!
Spring is come. I'm off for some fun.
Wheew!"

And away he blew down the High Street whirling and ancing and whistling and singing:

"Oh! ho! hee! hee! I laugh with glee,
I'm a merry Spring Wind,
Who'll dance with me?"

"We will," called the trees, and their branches all began ɔ dance and sway this way and that as they sang:

"Oh! ho! hee! hee! We laugh with glee.
We'll catch Willy Wind on the branch of a tree."

But they could not catch Willy Wind. On and on he ew.

"Wheew!
Oh! ho! hee! hee! I laugh with glee,
I'm a merry Spring Wind,
Who'll dance with me?"

"We'll dance with you," cried the clothes on the lothes-lines.

"We'll dance with you," called the newspapers at the tall on the corner.

"We'll dance with you," laughed the caps on the little oys' heads.

"We'll dance with you," shouted the lids on the dustbins hat were waiting to be emptied.

"We'll dance with you," whispered the curtains at the open windows.

And soon they were all dancing and twirling all over the place in a mad merry whirl.

"What a song and dance," cried the people in the street as they clutched at their hats and coats.

"Clanketty clank! Clanketty clank!" sang the dustbin lids as they whizzed down the hill.

"Wheew!" whistled Willy Wind at the top of his voice. "Wheew! Wheew!"

Presently he saw a garden filled with big yellow daffodils. "Oh! ho! hee! hee!" he whistled as he blew into the garden. "You golden daffodils, will you dance with me?" And soon the daffodils were dancing and whirling and laughing with Willy Wind. "Whoosh! Whoosh!" they sang, as they twirled this way and that.

Jeremy, the boy who lived at the house, looked out of his window and saw the daffodils dancing. "Mummy," he called, "please may I have my kite out in the garden? The wind is here and I want to have some fun."

And in a few moments Jeremy was dancing out with his kite in his hand. "Oh! ho! hee! hee!" cried Willy Wind. "A kite for me!" And off he whirled with the kite up, up, up into the blue sky.

The kite danced up and then down, this way and that, and Jeremy danced up and down, too, holding the string and laughing with all his might. Jeremy's dog, Flash, looked out of the window and saw the fun. "Wuff-wuff. Wuff-wuff," he barked. "Let me out, spring is here. I want to dance with the wind."

And soon Jeremy and Flash and the kite and the daffodils and Willy Wind were all dancing and singing and laughing together.

"Wuff-wuff," barked Flash. "What fun, what fun."

"Hooray," shouted Jeremy. "What fun, what fun."
"Whirr, whirr," sang the kite, and "Whoosh, whoosh,"
ent the daffodils, and "Oh! ho! hee! hee!" whistled
'illy Wind. "What fun, what fun."
Suddenly it was lunch-time and they all began to feel
red. Willy Wind floated the kite very gently back to
rth. The daffodils and Jeremy and Flash and Willy Wind
l stopped dancing together.
"Such rosy cheeks and bright eyes," smiled Mother,
she came out to fetch Jeremy and Flash in for lunch.
What fun you and Flash have had this morning romping
ith the wind."
"And my kite and the daffodils, too," added Jeremy.
We were all dancing together."
And, "What fun," echoed Willy Wind as he blew
mself slowly and softly home for a nice long rest.

The Cow that went for a Walk

Hilda Rostron

Buttercup was a brown-and-white cow. Every day, and twice a day, she went walking very slowly with all the other cows.

They went through the field gate, which squeaked with a very high squeak when it was opened, and down the little lane. Then they went through the farmyard gate, which squeaked with a very low squeak, and across the yard into the cowshed.

And in the cowshed the cows were milked.

Now Buttercup was always the first cow, and led all the other cows through the gates.

"Moo," she would say, "I'll show you the way."

And the cows would answer: "Moo-oo, we're coming."

One day after they had come back from milking, Buttercup saw that the field gate was not quite shut. "Moo-oo, someone has forgotten to fasten the gate," said Buttercup. "I'll go for a walk by myself. Moo-oo, I will indeed."

So she walked slowly over the field to the gate; pushed it open, just wide enough to get through.

"Squeak," went the gate in a very high voice, "and where may I ask are *you* going?"

"Moo-oo, I'm going for a walk by myself," said Buttercup, and she walked down the lane.

Tiddles the ginger cat was sitting on the farmyard gate, washing himself. He stopped licking his tail and stared at Buttercup.

"Miaow, and where may I ask are *you* going?"

"Moo-oo, I'm going for a walk by myself," said
uttercup, and she went on walking down the lane.

"Miaow," said Tiddles and went on washing himself.

There was a patch of very green grass by the side of the
ane, so Buttercup stopped and ate some. Just as she bent
own her head, she heard something scuffling and
nuffling in the hedge. It was a fat white puppy.

"Woof, woof, woof," he barked, "I'm burying a bone.
ook the other way. I don't want anyone to see where
bury my bones." So Buttercup looked the other way
while the puppy hid his bone. "Woof, thank you, I've
inished now," said the puppy. "Now you can look. Where
nay I ask are *you* going?"

"Moo-oo, I'm going for a walk by myself," said
Buttercup.

"Wuff, wuff, wuff," laughed the puppy and he began to
lig his bone up again.

Buttercup went on down the lane, thinking how nice
t was to be out for a walk by herself. Suddenly – "Cuckoo,
uckoo, cuckoo," called a cuckoo. He was perched on a
all tree over Buttercup's head. "Where may I ask are *you*
oing?"

"Moo-oo, I'm going for a walk by myself," answered
Buttercup.

"Cuckoo, cuckoo," laughed the cuckoo, and flew away.
Buttercup shook her head and went on, right to the end
of the lane.

Suddenly she heard someone shouting: "Hey! Where
lo you think *you* are going?"

"Oh dear," said Buttercup. "It's Farmer Brown. He
loesn't sound very pleased."

So Buttercup stopped and waited, and when Farmer
Brown got near she said: "Moo-oo; I'm going for a walk
by myself."

"Indeed you're not," said Farmer Brown. "You're going straight back to your field again. *And take all those other cows back with you!*"

Buttercup turned round, and there she saw all the other cows! They had followed her through the field gate that squeaked and down the lane.

"Moo," said Buttercup, "I thought that I was going for a walk by myself."

So Buttercup turned round, and walked past all the other cows until she was in front of them; and then they

urned round and followed her back to the field, on hrough the gate that squeaked. The gate said: "I *thought* you would soon be back. *You* can't go for a walk by ourself, Buttercup, the others *always* follow!"

Farmer Brown fastened the gate carefully after the cows were in. He was glad to have them all safely back in he field.

"Moo," said Buttercup, "well, it *was* a nice walk, even f you did all come with me."

"Moo-oo," said all the other cows, "Moo-oo."

Luke and Lucy; the Two Street Lamps

Phyllis Smith

Luke and Lucy were two street lamps. They lived in a little street with other lamps like themselves. Luke stood on one side of the street, and Lucy on the other.

Luke and Lucy were very good friends. They whispered to each other across the little street: "Putter, putter, putter, putter . . ."

Now all day long of course the street lamps rested. But all through the night their lights were bright. Then the little street was just like fairyland. Next to the little street was a big, big road. There were a lot of lamps on the big road, too. But they were not like the lamps in the little street. They were very tall and their lights were *very* bright. Many cars ran up and down the big road. They made *such* a noise: *Brr! Brr! Brrm! Toot! Toot!*

"I am so glad that we do not live in the big road," whispered Luke.

"So am I," whispered Lucy.

There were far too many cars on the big road, and some of them had to go into the little street.
When it was daylight they were all right. But when it was night they grumbled.

"This little street is not light enough."

"The lamps are not bright enough."

"We cannot see enough."

"We shall bump into one another."

Luke and Lucy were sorry for the cars, but there was nothing they could do.

Now one night there was a thick fog. The tall lamps in the big road were very bright, and their light could shine through the fog to show the way. So the cars were safe there. But in the little street the lamps were not bright enough. So the cars could not see enough. And they *did* bump into one another.

"Oh! Oh! Oh!" they cried. "The lamps in the big road are best. They have much brighter lights."

The tall lamps in the big road near the end of the little street said to Luke and Lucy: "You are no good. You will have to go."

"Where?" said Luke and Lucy.

One day soon after this, a big lorry came driving into the little street. "I have come to put new lamps in this street," he said "I have come to take the old lamps away."

"Oh, dear," said Luke and Lucy.

"Sorry," said the lorry, "it is my job to do it."

So that day a few new lamps were put up and a few old lamps taken away. The new lamps were very tall. They were just like the lamps in the big road.

That night the few new lamps shone in the little street. They had very bright lights.

When the cars came in from the big road, they said:

"Good! The little street will soon be light enough."

"The new lamps will be bright enough."

"Then we shall see enough. And we shall not bump into one another."

But Luke and Lucy whispered: "It is not like fairyland any more." And they were very sad.

Next day the lorry came back. "Now I have come for you," he said to Luke and Lucy.

First he took Luke, and Lucy was left all alone. But by and by the lorry came back. Then he took Lucy.

The lorry went on to the big road. There were so many cars. It was so noisy. *Brr! Brr! Brmm! Hoot! Hoot!*

Lucy lay in the lorry and thought: "Where is Luke? Where am I going?"

Soon the lorry stopped at a big yard. There were many other lamps in the yard, all on top of one another.

"Luke! Luke!" called Lucy.

But Luke was not there.

Day after day Lucy lay in the yard. Many other lamps were brought there, but not Luke.

One day a truck came to the yard. And with it came a man The man looked at all the lamps. Then he looked at Lucy.

"This is a good lamp," he said. "I will take it."

"Oh, dear," thought Lucy, "where will he take me?"

Well, first the truck went on to the big noisy road. *Brrm! Brrm! Hoot! Hoot!* But by and by he left it and drove along a quiet country road, with trees on either side. They looked down at Lucy and waved their leafy branches

"Have you seen Luke?" whispered Lucy.

And all the trees whispered to one another: "Have you seen Luke . . . seen Luke . . . seen Luke?"

All at once the truck stopped. "Out you go," he said.

So out Lucy went, lifted down by the man. She stood at the side of a little path and looked around. First she saw a beautiful house. Then she saw a lovely garden, with green lawns and many-coloured flowers.

"Oh," she said, "how wonderful! I wish Luke were here with me."

"I am," said Luke. "I am!"

And so he was – just on the other side of the path! They were so happy to be together again!

Luke and Lucy love their new home. They whisper to one another across the little path. "Putter . . . putter . . . putter . . . putter. . ." They rest all day. But at night their lights are bright.

Then the lovely garden is *just* like fairyland!

Mrs Gertie Goose's New Hat
Wilma Orchard

Mrs Gertie Goose loved buying new hats. She was a grey goose, so she usually bought grey hats to match her feathers. But the hats always had pretty trimmings on them.

Her spring hat was trimmed with buttercups and daises. In the summer her grey straw hat had pink roses all round the brim, and a pink veil over her eyes.

But now it was autumn, and on this bright afternoon she was wearing her new grey bonnet trimmed with a big bunch of red berries. It was tied under her chin with red velvet ribbons.

Mrs Goose held her head very high, and every now and then she gave it a little shake to make the berries move.

"What a pretty hat!" said a little voice. "I think it is the prettiest hat I've ever seen you wearing!".

Mrs Goose turned round and saw Katie Kitten looking at her new hat. She was very pleased. "Thank you, my dear," she said. "I have just bought it. It makes me feel quite gay!" And she shook her head again, so that Katie could see the berries move.

Just then the church clock struck five, and Mrs Goose said: "Oh dear, five o'clock, I must hurry! I did not mean to be so late. Goodbye, Katie."

Mrs Goose hurried down the road and turned off at the corner of the lane. She had her basket of shopping on one arm and her red umbrella on the other. She always carried an umbrella, even on sunny days.

As she walked along the lane, she noticed that it was getting rather windy. She felt the wind tugging at her new bonnet and she could feel the berries dancing about.

She walked a little faster and soon she reached Charlie the Cat's gate.

Charlie and Timothy Black Cat were busy in the garden making a big crackling bonfire. They were piling on wood and leaves and watching the flames and the blue smoke curling up very high.

As Mrs Gertie Goose passed the gate the wind gave a great big pull and one of her red velvet ribbons broke, and her bonnet fell right over her eyes. Poor Mrs Goose! She dropped her basket and out of it rolled some eggs and some oranges, and before she could push her bonnet back she had tripped over one of the oranges and sat down very hard! But she held on to her new grey bonnet.

"Help!" she squawked. "Help! Charlie!" When Charlie and Timothy heard her call they came running out of the gate. Charlie took one arm and Timothy the other and they helped her to her feet.

"Oh thank you, boys!" said Mrs Goose, "thank you very much." Then Charlie and Timothy picked up her umbrella and put her shopping back into the basket. One or two of the eggs were cracked, but not broken.

"There you are, Mrs Goose," said Charlie, "would you like Timothy and me to carry your basket and your umbrella home?"

"Yes please, boys," said Mrs Goose, "I must hold my bonnet on. Come back to my house and have something to eat."

So Charlie the Cat and Timothy walked one on each side of Mrs Goose. Charlie carried her basket and Timothy carried her umbrella, and Mrs Goose held on to her bonnet. When they came to her house she opened the door and they all went in. She took off her bonnet at once and had a good look at it.

"I think I shall be able to sew on the ribbon again," she

d. "The bunch of berries is still all right, I'm glad to
."

Then she unpacked her basket and said, "I won't take
ry long to get you something to eat. Would you like to
if your bonfire is all right and then come back and I
ll have something ready for you."

So Charlie and Timothy went back and had a look at
bonfire in Charlie's garden. It had burnt right down
d there were only a few red ashes left, so they raked it
d put some earth on it and then went back to Mrs
ose's house.

When Mrs Goose opened the door she was wearing her
st frilly apron and there was a most delicious smell.
ome in, boys," she said. "I have made something
ecial for you."

"Yes," said Charlie, "I think I can guess what it is."

"FISH AND CHIPS!" said Timothy.

"Quite right!" said Mrs Gertie Goose.

And they all had huge plates full of fish and chips for
pper!

Red Indian John
Anita Hewett

"I'm going to the woods to be a Red Indian," said John one day to his little dog Kim. "And on the way I must get some feathers. Red Indians always wear feathers."

"Woof!" barked Kim, and he wagged his stumpy tail. On their way down the lane they met a white goose. "Hello, Mrs Goose," said John. "I'm going to be a Red Indian. May I have some of your feathers, please?"

"Certainly not!" said the goose. "The idea!" And she snip-snapped her thick yellow beak. "I am proud of my fine white feathers, and you would only spoil them."

And on she walked down the lane.

"Oh dear! Now she's cross," sighed John. "I must ask someone else." At the end of the lane they saw a robin, singing on a holly bush. "Hello, Mr Robin," said John. "I'm going to be a Red Indian. May I have some of your feathers, please?"

"Certainly not!" said the robin. "The idea!" And he flicked his stiff little tail. "Winter is coming. I need all my feathers to keep myself warm."

And the robin went on singing.

"Oh dear! He doesn't care," said John. "We'll go into the woods, Kim. We may get some feathers there." In the woods, they saw a pigeon resting on a fir tree. "Hello, Mr Pigeon," said John. "I'm going to be a Red Indian. May I have some of your feathers, please?"

"Certainly not!" said the pigeon. "The idea." He looked down from his high perch. "I need all my feathers for flying."

Whirr went his wings, and away he flew.

"Oh dear! He's gone," said John. "Shall I ever get any
ıthers?"

John and Kim ran on between the trees, until they came
:ht through the wood and out at the other side. There
ey saw a farmyard with a stone wall around it, and a big
te. John looked over the gate, and little dog Kim
ɔked beneath it. They both saw a fat old turkey stepping
ross the farmyard.

"Oh, oh, oh! Look at Mr Turkey's feathers, Kim!" cried
hn. "They're big and strong and shiny, just right for a
:d Indian. But I don't suppose he'll let me have any."

All at once, a big black dog ran out of the woods. He
mped over the farmyard wall. He chased the poor fat
d turkey round and round the farmyard.

"Gobble, gobble, gobble," went the turkey.

John climbed over the gate quickly and little dog Kim squeezed quickly beneath it. John waved his arms at the big black dog. "Go away! Go away!" he shouted.

Kim snapped his little white teeth at the dog. "Woof, woof!" he barked.

The big black dog turned tail at once. He jumped over the wall, and ran away.

"Gobble, gobble, gobble," panted the turkey. "Thank you kindly. Now what can I do for *you*? I've nothing to give you, I'm afraid."

"Oh yes you have," said John. "Your feathers. Just one or two."

"My feathers? You wouldn't like *them*, would you?"

"That's just what I would like," John cried, and he clapped his hands. "Oh, Mr Turkey! Now I can be a Red Indian." So the turkey gave John ten fine feathers from hi tail.

"Oh *thank* you," said John, "what a lot – just you watc me Mr Turkey." Then John tied a piece of string around his head, and tucked the feathers into it.

"Look," he said, "now I'm a Red Indian – a Red Indian brave and I'm going to hunt in the forest."

"Grr, grr, grr," growled Kim, "grr, grr, grr."

"And you're a fierce brown bear," said John.

"Grr, grr, grr," growled Kim.

So that was how John got the feathers for his Red India head-dress. Then he and Kim went back out of the farmyard and played Red Indians all morning among the trees in the wood.

Piggy and Marmalade his Cat

May Brazier

One evening Piggy went to his pantry to fetch a fish for his little ginger cat's supper. But the fish dish was empty!

"Oh dear," he said. "I'm very sorry, Marmalade, I'm afraid that I forgot to buy a fish for your supper."

And Marmalade opened his mouth and wailed:

"Oh, Piggy, I do want a fish,
A nice little fish,
On plate or a dish,
For my supper."

"Well, don't worry, Marmalade," said Piggy. "We will go to the duck pond. There is sure to be plenty of fish in the pond."

So off went Piggy and Marmalade to the duck pond.

"Please," said Piggy to the duck, "could you catch a fish for my little ginger cat?"

"A fish?" quacked the duck. "No. I've finished fishing for today – but here's a piece of cake a little boy gave me. You can have that if you like."

"Thank you," said Marmalade, and although he ate the piece of cake, he said: "That was very nice.

"But I do want a fish,
A nice little fish,
On a plate or a dish,
For my supper."

"Let's go and ask the hen if she has any fish," said the duck.

So the duck, and Piggy, and Marmalade all went to see the hen.

"Henny Penny," quacked the duck to the hen, "have you a fish for this little ginger cat?"

"A fish?" clucked the hen. "Oh no, I never have fish. But here's a piece of pie a little girl gave me."

"Thank you," said Marmalade, and although he ate the piece of pie, he said: "That was very nice.

"But I do want a fish,
A nice little fish,
On a plate or a dish,
For my supper."

"Let's go and ask the farmyard cat," said the hen, "if she has any fish."

So the hen, and the duck, and Piggy, and Marmalade, went to see the farmyard cat.

Oh, Puss," clucked the hen to the farmyard cat, "have a fish for this little ginger cat?"

Oh no, I've eaten my fish," miaowed the farmyard cat, ıt here's a piece of cheese an old lady gave me."

Thank you," said Marmalade, but although he ate the ce of cheese, he said: "That was very nice.

"But I do want a fish,
A nice little fish,
On a plate or a dish,
For my supper."

Let's go and ask the dog," said the farmyard cat, "if he any fish."

o the farmyard cat, and the hen, and the duck, and gy, and Marmalade, all went to see the dog.

"Please, dog," miaowed the farmyard cat, "have you a fish for this little ginger cat?"

"Oh no, I don't like fish," barked the dog, "but here's a piece of meat the kind farmer gave me."

"Thank you," said Marmalade, but although he ate th piece of meat, he said: "That was very nice.

"But I do want a fish,
A nice little fish,
On a plate or a dish,
For my supper."

"Let's go and ask the farmer's wife," said the dog, "if she has any fish."

So the dog, and the farmyard cat, and the hen, and the duck, and Piggy, and Marmalade all went to see the farmer's wife.

"Mrs Farmer," barked the dog, "have you a fish for this little ginger cat?"

"Yes, I have a fish, a very nice fish," said the farmer's wife. "I will cook it at once for his supper."

And when the fish was cooked, the farmer's wife said:

"Here is your fish,
Your very nice fish,
On my best blue dish,
For your supper."

And then! What do you think Marmalade said? He said: "Oh dear, I don't want a fish for my supper now! I've eaten too much already!"

"Then the others must eat the nice fish from my best blue dish," said the farmer's wife.

So the dog ate a piece, and the farmyard cat ate a piece and the hen ate a piece, and the duck ate a piece, and Piggy ate a piece and said: "Well! We did find a fish for your supper, Marmalade!"

ary's Tree

'argaret Gore

e tree grew in a corner of the courtyard, just outside ry's window. It was the only tree for miles around; it od right in the middle of all the streets and houses and cks of flats. Gary lived in one of the blocks of flats – high on the seventh floor. The flats were so tall they made houses round about look like doll's houses.

Old Mrs Hopkins, who lived on the ground floor, told ry that long, long ago there had been no flats at all re, only fields and trees. Then the men had come along l cut down the trees and flattened the ground with their ldozers, so that they could start building. They had down every tree except this one.

Each morning when Gary opened his eyes the first thing saw was the tree – he could look straight into its topmost nches. "Hello, Tree," he said.

In summer the tree was green and full of light: it seemed be calling to him to go out: "It's going to be a beautiful y – get up out of bed and come and play!"

Then Gary would have his breakfast as quickly as ssible and run down to play with his friends from the er flats. They played what they called tree games. e of their favourites was the aeroplane game. They ran nd and round the tree with their arms outstretched. ey dived and they swooped; they took off and they ded; and as they went they made loud aeroplane ses.

One day Gary did not go down to play under the tree. did not feel well, so he had to stay in bed. His brother

Paul had just started school; Gary usually liked to stand at the window to wave goodbye, but this morning he did not feel well enough to bother.

Old Mrs Hopkins missed Gary during the day, and wh Paul came home from school, she called to him: "Where's Gary? I haven't seen him all day?"

"He had a sore throat this morning," replied Paul, "so he couldn't go out."

Gary was not at all well that night. He tossed and turne in bed: he was hot and sticky and uncomfortable. He did not think he would *ever* be able to go to sleep.

Then, outside his window, he heard a gentle, soothing, swishing sound. The wind was just stirring the topmost branches of the tree. The leaves rustled gently together as if someone were brushing them with a soft hairbrush. Gary knew his friend the tree was talking to him: "I'll ma you better – much, much better!" The leaves whispered: "Go to sleep . . . sleep . . . sleep!"

Gary thought they sounded like the sea breaking in little waves on the beach: he pretended he was dabbling his hands in the water, and he did not feel so hot. Then he grew drowsy, and at last he fell asleep.

When he awoke, it was morning, and there was his tree looking cool and green in the sunshine. Gary sat up in bed and he knew at once that he was better.

"Hello, Tree," he said. "I'm coming down to play aeroplanes today!"

he Ten Pussycats

ilary Stebbing

ce upon a time there were one, two, three, four, five, seven, eight, nine, ten little pussycats, who all lived ether in a big house. The two white pussycats made the ls, and did all the sweeping and polishing upstairs. e two black ones did the sweeping and polishing vnstairs. The two grey ones did the washing and ironing, two ginger ones laid the table and did the washing-up. e small tabby one did the cooking and the big tabby did all the shopping.

)ne day big Tabby Puss took his shopping basket and it down to the town on his tricycle.

'irst he went to the fish shop.

'Good morning, Mr Fishmonger," he said.

'Good morning, Tabby Puss," said the fishmonger, hat can I do for you?"

'Please can I have one, two, three, four, five, six, seven, ht, nine, ten little fishes for us pussies?"

'Certainly," said the fishmonger.

io Tabby Puss took the fishes and paid him, and then went on to the butcher.

'Good morning, Mr Butcher," he said.

'Good morning, Tabby Puss," said the butcher, "what I do for you?"

'Please can I have one, two, three, four, five, six, seven, ht, nine, ten bits of liver for us pussies?"

'Certainly," said the butcher.

io Tabby Puss took the liver and paid him and then went on to the dairy.

"Good morning, Mr Milkman," he said.

"Good morning, Tabby Puss," said the milkman, "wh can I do for you?"

"Please can I have one, two, three, four, five, six, seven, eight, nine, ten little bottles of milk for us pussies?"

"Certainly," said the milkman.

So Tabby Puss took the milk and paid him, and then h looked in his purse to see if he had any money left. "Ten pennies," he said to himself. "That's enough to buy a treat for us pussies." So he went into a shop and asked how much the sugar mice that he'd seen in the window co

"A penny each," said the shop-man.

"Very well," said Tabby Puss. "I'll have five pink ones and five white ones, please."

The shop-man put the sugar mice into ten little paper bags and Tabby Puss went off home with his basket of shopping.

When he reached home, the other nine pussies all crowded round him, purring and mewing and asking what he had bought.

"I've ten little fishes," said Tabby Puss. "Ten bits of iver, and ten little bottles of milk. *And* I've bought a treat for us all. Wait till I've put everything away in the larder. Then you shall have the treat."

So first Tabby Puss put everything away tidily. And hen he gave each of his pussy friends one of the little paper bags. When they opened them, how delighted they all were to find a pink or a white mouse.

One black, one white, one grey and one ginger puss decided to keep theirs until after lunch. But the other black and the other white and the other grey and the other ginger and the little tabby puss nibbled off the heads. And what did big Tabby Puss do? He ate up all his sugar mouse in one mouthful.

Weren't those one, two, three, four, five, six, seven, eight, nine, ten lucky little pussycats?

The Boy with Red Shoes

Leila Berg

Once upon a time there was a little boy with bright red shoes.

One day he went out in his bright red shoes and put one foot right into a puddle. And his shoe stuck fast in the mud!

He pulled and he pulled and his foot came out of the shoe but the shoe stuck fast in the mud, and the little boy couldn't get it out again.

So now he had only one shoe. A bright red shoe, and a very nice shoe; but still – only one.

And he had to hop. Hop, hop, hop, he went down the road. Hop, hop.

And as he hopped, he cried a little. Although he was a big boy, nearly four, he cried a little, because he had left his other red shoe stuck in the mud. And now he had only one nice red shoe. And that's why he cried.

He passed some birds sitting on a gate. "Why do you cry, why do you cry?" said the birds.

"Because I have only one shoe," said the little boy.

"Only one shoe,
What shall I do?"

"Hop along," cried the birds, and they flew into a tree. So he hopped!

By and by he came to a cat. He was sitting on a wall awa from the wet, watching the birds. "Why do you cry, why, why?" said the cat.

"Because I've left my shoe in the mud." said the little boy.

"I've only one shoe,
What shall I do?"

"Hop along," said the cat, and it arched its back.
o he hopped!

Soon he came to a dog, playing with a stick. It took
ıe stick in its mouth and it shook it: whack! whack!
hack! whack!

But when it saw the boy hopping, it put the stick down.
Why are you crying, little boy?" it said. "Why, why,
hy, why, why?"

"I'm crying because my shoe's stuck fast in the mud of
puddle.

"I've only one shoe,
What shall I do?"

"Hop along," said the dog. "Hop along." So he
opped!

And at last he came to a kind lady, who was sweeping
er step. "Why are you crying, little boy?" she said. "Has
omething bad happened?"

"Yes indeed it has," said the little boy. "I've left my
hoe in the mud of a puddle, and now I have only one nice
ed shoe. That's why I'm crying.

"Only one shoe,
What can I do?
Boo hoo hoo."

"Goodness, gracious, what an awful noise!" said the lady. "That won't help at all. We'll go right back, and get the shoe. That's what we'll do."

So back they went. The lady held the little boy's hand. And the little boy went hop, hop, in his one shoe. But the lady went tip-tap, tip-tap, in her shiny brown ones.

And soon they reached the puddle. The lady rolled up her sleeve and put her hand down into the water and pulled the shoe out of the mud. "Here we are," she said. "It's black and wet and dirty now. But we can take it home and dry it and polish it and make it red again."

So they went home, and first they washed the shoe till it looked red again. And then they put the shoe in the sun

till it was dry again. Then they polished it till it was shining again and looked just like the other red shoe. Then the little boy put it on and he didn't have to hop any more. He went tap tap in his two red shoes, his two pretty red shoes, his two *clean* shiny red shoes.

(And after that he never went in puddles again, unless he had his Wellingtons on.)

Published in *Lollipops* (Brockhampton Press).

Kurlie Kitten's Curious Morning

Ruth Paine

Kurlie was a pretty little grey kitten whose fur was soft and curly all over, and that is why the family called her Kurlie.

Her own special home was a comfortable round basket made as soft as soft could be with an old blue woollen shawl. If the weather was cold, Mother put her basket down in front of the fire, and if the weather was warm and sunny, Mother put it on the kitchen window-sill, and at night Mother always put it ready for her at the bottom of the kitchen cupboard. When Kurlie was tired of playing, she would run and climb into her basket and curl round and go fast asleep. It was her very own special basket home.

So you see, she was a lucky kitten and she purred a great deal to show how happy she was.

But, one May morning, she woke up feeling very strange and excited. Her paws itched and her ears twitched, her whiskers flicked and her fur tingled all over. She stretched twice and yawned once and jumped out of her basket. She said, "Horrid old basket!" and, "Nasty old blue shawl!" Then she jumped up on the window-sill and looked out into the garden. Her paws itched and her ears twitched, her whiskers flicked and her fur tingled all over.

"I wonder why I feel so excited?" she said to herself. "I feel I want to be grown-up and to get out and about and see how other people live. I am sure their homes are much nicer than my old basket!"

So she jumped down from the window-sill and mewed

at the back door, and very soon Mother came and opened it for her.

"Crazy little kitten!" said Mother as she watched Kurlie scampering up the garden path, with her paws itching and her ears twitching, her whiskers flicking and her fur tingling all over.

The early morning air was fresh and clear and Kurlie danced on her small grey paws up the garden path until she came to the lilac bush. There, between two twigs, hung the prettiest thing she had ever seen. It seemed to be a circle of finest silver lace, dangling by silver threads and shining with tiny diamonds in the early morning sunshine.

"Now, whatever is that pretty thing?" said Kurlie curiously, stopping suddenly in her dance. Just at that moment a big brown spider came running up one of the silver threads.

"Hello, can I help you?" the spider enquired.

"I was just wondering what this lovely silver circle is," said Kurlie.

"This web? Why, it is my home," said the spider.

"Your home?" said Kurlie, in surprise, and she put out one paw and touched it. The dewdrops scattered as her tiny sharp claws caught in the fine threads, and the web was shattered.

"Just *look* what you have done," said the spider. "I spent all yesterday afternoon making that web and now you

have broken it and I shall have to begin all over again. Oh, it is a shame!"

"I am very sorry," said Kurlie. But the spider was already busy spinning more silver threads.

So Kurlie skipped on, with her tiny grey tail held high, thinking to herself, "That was a very pretty home. Fancy an old brown spider living in such a pretty house! But it wouldn't suit me. It is much too delicate. Why, it broke with one touch of my paw! I like my basket much better."

She scampered on up the path until she came to the old brick wall at the very end, and there, two bricks up, she saw a round, brownish-grey shell.

"Now, whatever is that?" said Kurlie curiously, her blue eyes as big as saucers. A tiny, soft head with tiny, waggling horns peeped out of the shell.

"Good morning," said the snail, "what are you staring at?"

"I was just wondering what this round thing could be. I didn't know you lived in it! Can you come out and play?"

"No, I can't come out as you say," answered the snail, "because I carry my house around on my back, *always*."

Then he climbed very, very slowly up the wall dragging his home with him.

"Fancy having to carry your house around on your back! I'm glad I don't have to carry my basket on my back everywhere I go!" thought Kurlie as she ran on, skipping along by the wall, her paws itching and her ears twitching, her whiskers flicking and her fur tingling all over, until she came to the garden gate. She measured the space between the bars with her small whiskers, and then slipped through.

She crossed the lane outside and looked into the ditch below the bank. There in the ditch was a big black stone.

"Now, I wonder what that is?" said Kurlie, pushing her little pink nose under it.

"It is usual to knock before looking into other people's houses," said the wrinkly old toad who was sitting in a little scooped-out hollow underneath the stone.

"Oh, I beg your pardon," said Kurlie, backing away quickly, "I had no idea you were there."

"Your apology is accepted," said the toad. "Welcome to my humble home."

"I'm sorry I haven't time to stay this morning," said

Kurlie, "I'll come some other day." And she skipped up the bank, saying to herself, "Fancy living under a nasty, black stone in a ditch! I much prefer my warm basket."

As Kurlie went skipping and jumping along the bank, she came at length to a dark hole in the ground, half hidden by the roots of a tree.

"Now, I wonder what that is?" she said, making a sideways dart at it, and sniffing cautiously. It was dark inside, and seemed to go down a very long way. She was just deciding it didn't look as interesting as she had at first thought, when a brown rabbit popped up out of it.

"Shh!" said the rabbit. "My babies are all asleep down there. Go away from my front door."

"So that's *her* home," thought Kurlie, scampering off. "I should be very sorry to live in a nasty hole, right under the ground. My basket is really much more comfortable."

So Kurlie skipped back down the lane, squeezed between the bars of the gate and trotted down the garden path.

A white butterfly fluttered above her head. Kurlie wanted to play with it, and she leapt high up in the air to catch it in her two tiny grey paws, but it dodged away light as laughter, and settled on a red peony.

"Where do *you* live?" asked Kurlie.

"Here, there and everywhere, mostly under a cabbage-leaf," said the butterfly, and fluttered lightly away to a bed of pink tulips.

"Fancy living here, there and everywhere, but mostly under a cabbage-leaf," said Kurlie to herself as she ran down the last little bit of the path and mewed outside the back door.

"You've been a long way this morning," Mother greeted her as she let her in, and she noticed that a rather tired little kitten had come home. Her paws did not itch, her ears did not twitch, her whiskers did not flick and her fur was no longer tingling all over.

Kurlie rubbed round Mother's ankles and purred loudly as she was given a saucer of cool milk, and, after a refreshing drink, she went straight to her cosy basket – her very own little round basket with the soft blue shawl in it. There she carefully licked her tiny grey paws and her curly grey fur, and then she settled down for a little nap until dinner-time.

The Dutch Doll

Ruth Ainsworth

Once upon a time there was a little girl called Jenny.

One day her uncle gave her a shining fivepenny piece and she carried it about with her, tied in the corner of her handkerchief.

"Will you buy some sweets?" asked her father.

"Will you buy a book?" asked her mother.

"No," said Jenny and shook her head. She knew what she was going to buy. She was going to buy a Dutch doll.

In the town where Jenny lived there was a market every Saturday. The market people came and set up tables and stalls right in the middle of the main street and on these they put all kinds of things to sell – fish and flowers and eggs and cabbages and clothes and books and toys.

Jenny loved going to the market, and there was one stall she liked better than all the others. It belonged to an old lady. Every Saturday she sat there and sold Dutch dolls. All costing exactly fivepence each.

When Saturday came, Jenny asked her mother to take her to the market, so that she could choose her Dutch doll. Mother held her hand and they made their way through the crowds till they came to the old lady with her Dutch dolls.

The Dutch dolls had wooden heads and wooden bodies and wooden arms and wooden legs. Their arms were jointed at the elbow so that they could move up and down. The legs were jointed at the knee, so that they could move too.

Each doll had black shining hair painted on her flat wooden head, and black eyes and red lips, and a dab of red on each cheek as well. And a sharp little wooden nose sticking out in the middle of her face.

Jenny looked at them all and wondered which she should choose. "Hurry up and choose, Jenny," said Mother. "They are all just the same."

Oh dear, Jenny did not know which doll she liked best! One had specially red cheeks. Another had specially black hair. Then she noticed one that had a sad look on her face. Jenny stared at her a long time. She looked as if she were lonely. "I'll have *this* one please," said Jenny, and she picked up the sad-faced doll. She untied the knot in the corner of her handkerchief and took out the money and gave it to the old lady.

"I shall call my Dutch doll Greta," said Jenny as they hurried away. Now on the way home they had to cross a bridge over the river. Jenny stopped, because she liked to look down at the boats and the swans in the water below. "Look Greta," she said, and held the little Dutch doll up so that she could see too. "Look at the boats and the two big swans. Aren't they nice?"

But Greta still looked sad.

Suddenly, someone who was walking by bumped into Jenny and Greta fell out of her hand, over the railing of the bridge, down, down, down till she hit the water – splash!

"Oh!" cried Jenny. "Oh! She's gone! Greta's fallen in the water!"

Then Jenny heard another splash. A big black dog jumped into the water from the side of the river and swam towards Greta. He thought Jenny had thrown a stick in for him, and he liked getting sticks out of the water. Because Greta was made of wood, she floated on the top of the

water. Soon the dog reached her and took her in his mouth and swam back to the side of the river where his master was waiting for him.

He jumped out and shook himself, "Brr brr," and then he laid Greta at his master's feet. He wagged his tail proudly and his master patted his wet head and said, "Good dog! Good dog!"

"Wuff, wuff," said the big black dog, for he wanted his master to throw Greta in again.

But his master said, "No – good dog – lie down," then they waited for Jenny and her mother to come.

Jenny hurried over the bridge and ran fast along the

le of the river. When she got to the man she bent down
ıd patted the big dog's wet head and said: "Thank you
r saving Greta; she's only new today."

"I'm afraid my dog's teeth have made some marks on
ur new doll and scratched off some of her paint, but if
u'll let me keep her till tomorrow I'll make her as good
new. Where do you live?"

"Ivy Cottage, just along the road there," said Jenny,
ıd she pointed so that he'd know the way.

"Leave her with me today," said the man, "and I'll
ing her back on my way past your house tomorrow."

"Thank you," said Jenny, though she knew she'd miss

Greta badly, and would rather have taken her home even if she was scratched a bit.

That afternoon Jenny made a nice bed all ready for Greta out of a shoe-box, and she made some toy food for her – red apples and white eggs and yellow buns.

And next morning, sure enough, the front-door bell rang, and there was the man with the big black dog. He handed Jenny a brown paper parcel and said, "There she is, young lady, as good as new."

"Thank you," said Jenny. "Would your dog like a bone for his dinner? We kept one for him."

"Yes," said the man. "He would."

So Jenny gave him a big, juicy bone, wrapped up in paper, and he went away.

And then Jenny undid her parcel and took out Greta and had a good look at her.

"Oh, Greta," she said. "Your hair is blacker than it was, and your cheeks are redder, *and you've got a smile*. You don't look sad any more. Did you like falling in the river then? Did it cheer you up?"

But Greta just went on smiling and looking happy, so Jenny put her to sleep in the nice new bed she had made for her.

Published in *Listen with Mother Tales* (William Heinemann Ltd).

ittle Miss Pig

erbert McKay

is a fine day," said Mr Pig. "I think I will go for a walk
l call on Little Miss Pig." So he took down his hat, and
k up his stick, and off he went.

Ie went down the lane, and waved his stick happily as
walked along. At last he came to a neat little house with
eat little front garden. "This is where Little Miss Pig
:s," he said. "I will ring the bell and see if she is at
ne." He opened the neat little gate, and went along the
ıt little path, and he rang the bell.

Then he rang the bell again. But still no one came to
: door.

'Little Miss Pig must be out," said Mr Pig. "She may
ve gone to the wood to gather nuts. I will go to the wood
l help her." He waved his stick, and off he went once
re.

On and on went Mr Pig till he came to the wood. He
led out: "Little Miss Pig! Little Miss Pig! Are you in
: wood gathering nuts?"

But no one answered him. He called again: "Little Miss
;! Little Miss Pig!"

And still no one called back.

'Little Miss Pig is not in the wood," said Mr Pig. "She
.y have gone to the shop to get some tea and a cake and
ot of jam. If I go to the shop I can carry them home for
:." On he went once more.

When Mr Pig reached the shop he said: "Mr Shop-man,
; Little Miss Pig been here? Did she come to get some
. and a cake and a pot of jam?"

"No, Mr Pig," said the shop-man, "she has not been here. I have not seen her today."

"Hm, she may have gone to the mill on top of the hill," said Mr Pig. "She may have gone for a bag of flour, to make pastry for a pie. I will certainly carry it home for her." And off he went again, away up the hill.

When Mr Pig came to the mill he said: "Mr Miller, did Little Miss Pig come here today for a bag of flour for making pie-crust?"

"No, Mr Pig," said the miller. "I have not seen her today."

"Hm, perhaps she has got back home now," said Mr Pig. "I will go back to her house, and ring the bell, and see." So back he went to Miss Pig's house.

When he came to the house where Little Miss Pig lived he rang the bell. Little Miss Pig opened the door.

Mr Pig gave her a big smile and said: "Little Miss Pig,

there you are! I came to your house and rang the bell, and you were not in."

"Oh!"

"I wondered if you were gathering nuts and wanted me to help you."

"Oh no!"

"And then I wondered if you were getting tea and a cake and a pot of jam to ask me to tea! And then I wondered if you were getting a bag of flour to make the crust of a pie."

"Oh no! I got those things yesterday," said Little Miss Pig. "I made the pie this morning, and it is on the table with the cake and the jam. Now I am just going to make tea. Come in, Mr Pig! And after tea we can have the nuts."

"Little Miss Pig," said Mr Pig with a *very* big smile, "I am so glad I came."

Tippy Finds a Friend
Jean English

Tippy was a tipper wagon. Not one of the really big ones, but one of the quite small tipper wagons, with two wheels at the front and two double wheels at the back. He was painted bright orange, and his driver's name was Bob. One morning when Tippy and his friends had just woken up and were waiting to see what work was to be done, the Contractor came into their garage. The Contractor was an important man. He was in charge of all the wagons, cement mixers and bulldozers.

"Good morning, boys," he said, rubbing his hands together. "We're starting a big new job today, there'll be plenty of work for everybody."

"Are we going to carry loads of paving stones to the new housing estate?" asked Spike, a medium-sized wagon.

"Or loads of sticky black tarmac to mend the roads?" asked Mike, his twin, who rather liked getting dirty.

"No, no," said the Contractor. "There's going to be a new pond over in the park, and we're going to help them dig the big hole for it."

"Oh good," said Tippy happily. "Do you want me to take all the workmen with their picks and spades over to the park, Mr Contractor?" He liked taking the gangs of noisy, joking workmen out to a big job.

"No, no, Tippy. We shan't need many workmen on this job. And we shan't need picks and spades."

"But you'll have to dig a pretty big hole for a new pond, surely sir," said Bob, Tippy's driver, who'd just joined them.

"We'll need a big hole, yes," the Contractor smiled. "And I've got just the man for the job. A new machine, Bob, an excavator. I've just bought it. Come and have a look."

Bob and the Contractor went out, and as they left the door open, the wagons looked out with interest to see the new machine.

"He's got metal caterpillar tracks, like me," said Barry the Bulldozer.

"And he's got a big shovel thing in front," said Tippy. "I suppose he uses that to scoop up all the earth. He looks very shiny and new."

"He looks snooty," said Spike.

"And stuck up," said Mike.

But that was all the talking they had time for. Soon they were all going out to the park, and they worked very hard right through the day. The new machine, the excavator, was certainly very quick. He would dig out a big scoop of earth, then turn his shovel round on its long arm, swing it over to Tippy, standing waiting, and THUD! Down would come the earth onto the little wagon's back. Then the long arm would swing back. Dig, swing, and THUD! Dig, swing, and THUD! It didn't take long to fill Tippy, and he would hurry away with his load to the tip on the other side of town, while another wagon – Spike or Mike – would hurry up beside the new machine to get his load of soil.

In the garage that night, as all the tired wagons rested, ready for sleep, Tippy, trying to be friendly, said to the new excavator: "You worked very hard today, didn't you? What a lot of soil you can move."

"Yes. I'm the very latest model," said the excavator. "I can do the work of a whole gang of men. Soon there'll probably be no need for workmen at all. All the digging will be done by first-class modern machines like me."

Mike looked across at Tippy. "I told you he was stuck up," he whispered.

"And snooty," whispered Spike.

"Ssh," said Tippy. "Don't be unkind, you two." But he felt rather sad to think that soon there might be no more noisy workmen to carry on his back.

Next morning, the Contractor came into the garage early and called: "Good morning, boys. Lots more diggin to do today."

The excavator spoke up. "Right. I'm ready for work, sir."

"Oh," said the Contractor, "we shan't be needing you today, my boy."

"But you said there was lots of digging to do," said the the excavator.

"Yes, so there is, but not the easy soft soil that we had yesterday, I'm afraid. We've come to some awkward patches of hard rock, and before we can move that, we'll have to get to work with picks and spades."

Tippy brightened up. "A load of workmen to take out, Mr Contractor? I'm ready."

"So am I," said Bob, climbing up into the driver's seat. "I'll just drive you out into the yard, Tippy."

Tippy purred out to the yard. There was a crowd of noisy, smiling workmen waiting there. They lifted up a great pile of picks and spades, and dumped them with crashes and bangs onto the little wagon's back. Then they all climbed aboard, and shouted to Bob, "Ready? Off we go."

Tippy set off for the park, and he felt so happy to have the friendly workmen riding with him, that he began to sing:

"Oh you pick a pick, I'll pick a pick,
We'll all pick a pick together.
You pick a pick and I'll pick a pick,
In fair or stormy weather."

When the day's work was over, and the wagons got back the garage that night, they found the new excavator oking rather sorry for himself. The dreary day spent shut in the garage by himself had made him feel rather iserable, and he was very glad to welcome the wagons ome. He did his best to be friendly. He told Tippy that ere would probably always be plenty of work for eryone, for the men with their picks and spades, as well for the big excavators.

"I do hope so," said Tippy sleepily. "I heard the ontractor say there'd be some ordinary soil for you to dig morrow. So you'll be able to come out to the park with , I expect."

"That will be nice," said the excavator. "Good night, ippy."

"Good night – oh," said Tippy, "I don't know your ame."

"You can call me Digger."

"Right. Then good night, Digger. See you in the orning."

Nothing to do
Betty Coombs

Once upon a time there was a little girl called Ann.

One summer afternoon she had nothing to do. So she went to find Mother. Her mother was busy at the sewing machine, making Ann a new blue dress.

Whirr! Whirr! Whirr! went the machine.

"I need another reel of cotton to finish your dress," said Mother. "Would you like to go down to Miss Peters' shop and buy one for me, please?"

"Oh yes," said Ann, "I've nothing to do this afternoon."

Ann took a tenpenny bit in one hand and a small piece of cloth in the other. "If you hold the cloth against the reel of cotton," said Mother, "you will be sure to get the right colour."

So off went Ann out of the house and up the village street. Ann opened the door of Miss Peters' shop. It was cool and rather dark inside. Ann could smell apples and sweets and potatoes all at the same time. You see, Miss Peters sold all kinds of things in her little village shop.

"Please, Miss Peters," said Ann. "Mummy wants a reel of cotton *this* colour," and she held out the piece of cloth.

Miss Peters put a box full of coloured reels on the counter. Ann held her piece of cloth against one reel. No, that was too light. She held it against another. No, that was too dark. She held it against another. Yes! That was exactly right.

Miss Peters took out the reel. Ann handed over the tenpenny bit and Miss Peters put the reel of cotton and the change in a little piece of brown paper. She screwed it tightly at one end and then at the other.

"Could you do something for me, Ann?" said Miss Peters.

"Oh yes," said Ann, "I'd like to. I've nothing to do this afternoon."

"Mrs Brown's chicken food has just arrived," said Miss Peters. "Would you take it along to her, please?"

"Will you keep my cotton reel and change till I come back?" said Ann.

"Yes, of course," said Miss Peters, and she put the little parcel under the counter.

Ann took the chicken food and went out of the shop and up the village street.

"Hello, Ann," said Mrs Brown, as she opened her door, "how kind of you to bring the chicken food. Would you ike to collect the eggs for me while I feed the hens?"

"Yes please," said Ann, "I've nothing to do this afternoon."

So Mrs Brown gave Ann a small green basket to put he eggs in, and they went to the hen house. Ann put her and in the warm nests in the hen house and collected ne . . . two . . . three . . . four . . . five . . . six white eggs and ne large brown egg.

"Thank you, Ann," said Mrs Brown. "Now I wonder you would take this box of eggs to Mrs Green for me?"

"Oh yes," said Ann, "I've nothing to do this afternoon."

So off went Ann again, a little more slowly this time, for he was carrying the box of eggs very carefully. Mrs Green as standing high up on a ladder picking plums from her lum tree.

"Hello, Mrs Green," shouted Ann.

"Hello, Ann," said Mrs Green. "Have you brought y box of eggs? That is kind of you."

Then Mrs Green came down the ladder and said: "I'm going to make some jam for Mrs White, but I haven't quite enough jars to put it in. Could you go and get them for me, Ann?"

"Oh yes," said Ann, "I've nothing to do this afternoon."

So off went Ann, once again, with an empty basket for the jam-jars. When Mrs White opened the door Ann smelt a lovely smell of newly-baked shortbread.

"Hello, Ann," said Mrs White.

"Can you let Mrs Green have some jam-jars, please?" said Ann.

"Yes, of course," said Mrs White, "come in and I'll get them."

Ann sat down and presently Mrs White came back with six jars in the basket and on top of them was a little paper packet.

"That," said Mrs White, "is a piece of shortbread for your tea."

"Oh, thank you," said Ann. "Goodbye, Mrs White."

Back she went down the village street. She gave the jars to Mrs Green, who said: "Thank you, Ann – here are some plums for your tea and here is the empty egg-box to take back to Mrs Brown."

"Thank you," said Ann. "Goodbye." Back she went down the village street. She gave the empty egg-box to Mrs Brown, who said: "Thank you, Ann. Here is a brown egg in a little paper bag with your name written on it."

"Thank you," said Ann. "Goodbye."

So off she went down the village street, till she reached Miss Peters' shop.

"Thank you for helping me, Ann," said Miss Peters. "Here's your little parcel."

"I don't think I can carry it as well as all these things," said Ann.

"My goodness," said Miss Peters, "I'll see what I can find to put them in." She went into her little room at the back of the shop and came back with a little basket.

"You can have this, Ann. I used to play with it when I was a little girl."

"Oh, thank you, Miss Peters," said Ann. She put the shortbread and the plums and the brown egg and her little parcel with her reel of cotton and the change in the basket. "Goodbye, Miss Peters," said Ann. "Thank you for the *lovely* basket. I've had plenty to do this afternoon, after all!"

No Dinner for Sammy

Lavender Littlejohn

One morning young Sammy Frog sat with his mother at the edge of the big round pond.

"What have we got for dinner today, Mum?" asked young Sammy.

"Worms and water-weeds," croaked Mrs Fanny Frog.

"Oh, I'm tired of worms and water-weeds," said Sammy. "I think I'll go off to look for something more interesting."

So he dived into the pond with a great big SPLOSH, swam to the other side and with a leap, and a jump, and a hop, he was in a field of long grass. With two more leaps, he

landed right behind Tommy, the old donkey, who was slowly swishing the flies away with his tail.

Swish, swish, swish, swish.

"Hello! Have you something good for dinner today?" croaked Sammy.

"Hee haw," chuckled Tommy when he saw who was peaking to him.

"Something good did you say, young frog? I've a few histles and some grass. Will you join me?"

"No thank you," croaked Sammy, "thistles would rick my throat and grass is much too tough."

And off he went with big leaps and jumps and hops, ill he came to a broad oak tree. There he stopped for a est in the shade. Just then Sammy heard a rustle of eaves above him, and there was Peter, the grey squirrel, ooking down at him with his bright beady eyes.

"Where are you going?" said Peter in his squeaky oice.

"I'm looking for a different kind of dinner," croaked ammy, "I'm tired of worms and water-weeds."

"You can share my nuts if you like. I'm just going to tch some from my larder," said Peter.

"Oh no," said Sammy, "nuts would be too dry and ard for me."

But he thanked Peter and then he set off again with big aps and jumps and hops, till he spied Mrs Emily Rabbit, tting on a bank munching a round turnip.

"You're a long way from home," said Mrs Rabbit, have a bite of turnip with me."

Sammy squatted down on the bank with Mrs Rabbit, d stared hard at the turnip with his large round eyes, t he just couldn't fancy turnip somehow!

"I'll have to look somewhere else for my dinner," said.

So he left Mrs Rabbit, and hopped down the bank and landed in a long dusty lane.

With big leaps, and jumps, and hops he went down the lane, which seemed to Sammy to go on and on for ever, and his leaps, and his jumps and his hops got slower and slower and *slower*. Quite suddenly he stopped, and sat very still in the middle of the lane.

"I don't know where I am!" panted Sammy to himself. "Oh, I wish I was back home."

Before long he heard voices and, looking round, he saw a little girl and her daddy coming towards him. The little girl, who was called Joanna, was carrying a basket full of wild flowers that she had been picking.

"Oh Daddy, do come and see, here's a frog in the road," Joanna cried. "Poor little thing, I believe he's lost!"

Poor Sammy felt so tired he didn't try to move. Farmer Davis (for that's what Joanna's father was called) looked down at Sammy.

"He's strayed a long way from home," he said, "I expect he lives by the pond, frogs always live near water. We pass the pond on the way back. I think we'd better take him home again."

"Oh yes, do let's! I can carry him in my basket," said Joanna.

Sammy let Joanna pick him up and put him gently in amongst her wild flowers. Then she and her daddy walked along the lane for a little way. Then they turned off through a gate, and went up a path and into a field.

Sammy felt quite safe in Joanna's basket, and by and by he peeped over the top of it, and saw Tommy the old donkey in the distance still swishing the flies away with his tail.

Swish, swish, swish, swish.

"Thank goodness," thought Sammy, "that means I'm nearly home!"

When Farmer Davis and Joanna reached Tommy, they stopped so that Joanna could give him a pat. At once Tommy put his nose into Joanna's basket hoping that she might have a carrot for him. He did get a surprise when he saw Sammy there instead!

At the edge of the pond Joanna lifted Sammy out of her basket and popped him down into the cool long grass.

"Goodbye, little frog," she said. "Don't you get lost again, will you?"

Almost at once Sammy dived into the pond with a great big SPLOSH and swam to the other side.

"Mum, Mum," he croaked loudly, as he climbed out of the water, "I am so hungry, can I have my worms and water-weeds right away?"

Mrs Frog was sitting on a log, enjoying the warm sunshine. She looked surprised when she heard Sammy was hungry.

"Dear me," she croaked. "I thought you were going to find a different sort of dinner today! Your cousin Harry came to see me and I'm afraid I gave him your share."

"Oh dear!" Sammy said. "I'm ever so hungry!"

"Cheer up," said Mrs Frog, "I've collected a fresh insect and water-weed salad, and in a few minutes you can have some for your tea."

Christopher's Friend

Jean Sutcliffe

Christopher often went to stay with his Grandmother. One of the reasons he liked going was that he usually saw Mr Warren.

Christopher was very fond of Mr Warren. He came to do Grandmother's garden twice a week. He did the digging in the winter. And he planted the potatoes and cabbages and peas and beans in the spring. He clipped the hedges and mowed the grass. In fact he did all the jobs that were too heavy for Grandmother to do now that she was getting old.

But the reason Christopher liked Mr Warren so much was that he was a fireman. He was actually the driver of the fire engine. So you see, he was a *particularly* interesting man, wasn't he? Christopher used to talk to him for hours. Mr Warren lived in a little house next door to the fire station. So whenever Christopher went to the shops with Grandmother, he'd say: "Can we go past the fire station, please, and can I stay there while you do the shopping?"

And Grandmother nearly always said: "Yes."

So now you see why Christopher liked specially to visit his Grandmother.

One day a most exciting thing happened. Christopher was standing at the open door of the fire station looking at the big red fire engine.

When he'd had a really good look he called out: "Hello Mr Warren? Are you there?"

"Hello, Christopher," said another man. "He's not here, he's just gone home."

So Christopher went and knocked on Mr Warren's door, and when Mrs Warren opened it he said: "Grandma said I was to give this note to Mr Warren."

"Come in, Christopher," said Mrs Warren. "We're just having a cup of tea. P'haps you'd like one."

"Thank you," said Christopher, "I am a bit thirsty."

So he went into the kitchen. Mr Warren said: "Good morning, Christopher! So you're postman today are you? Sit down."

While Christopher was drinking his tea, Mr Warren read the note . . . and then . . . before he could say anything about it . . . a bell began to ring.

"Fire alarm," said Mr Warren. "I'm off!"
And he was out of the house in a twinkling!

"Oh," said Christopher, "oh, Mrs Warren, is he going to a fire?"

"Yes," said Mrs Warren, "would you like to watch the engine going out?"

"I would," said Christopher.

"Come upstairs then," said Mrs Warren. "We can see it from the bedroom window."

They ran upstairs like lightning and were only just in time to see the big red fire engine coming out into the street.

Mr Warren was driving it. He had a fireman's helmet on his head.

Down the street two other firemen came running, buttoning their coats as they ran. They swung themselves up onto the fire engine and one caught a rope and pulled the big shiny brass bell. Off went the fire engine at top speed. Everyone got out of its way as it rushed along clanging its bell.

Then out of the station came another engine with more firemen, and long hose-pipes for squirting the water on the fire.

"Oh," said Christopher. "How quickly they've gone!"

"Can't waste any time when there's a fire," said Mrs Warren. "Now, Christopher, there's your Grannie looking for you. Off you go, or she'll think you're lost."

So Christopher ran downstairs out of the front door. And all the way home he told his Grandmother about what he'd seen. "It was a real fire, Grannie," he said. "And they've just gone to put it out with water. I saw the long hose-pipes for the water and the long ladders and the firemen and Mr Warren was driving the fire *engine*."

"My, you are a lucky boy," said Grandmother. "I've lived here for twenty years and I've never seen the fire engine going out to a real fire."

"I'll ask Mr Warren all about it when he comes tomorrow," said Christopher. And he did.

Published in *Jacko and Other Stories* (Bodley Head).

Christopher the Fireman
Jean Sutcliffe

Well, the morning after Christopher had seen the fire engine and the trucks with the hoses and ladders going off to put out a real fire, he ran down the garden to see if Mr Warren had come yet, because he wanted to ask him all about it.

"Mr Warren!" he called. "Mr Warren! Are you there?"

But there was no answer, so he sat down on a wheelbarrow under an apple tree and waited, for he knew Mr Warren was coming for sure. It was very quiet in the garden, but a thrush was singing and a bee was buzzing and somewhere a cock was crowing and then the church clock struck half-past nine.

Ah! There was Mr Warren, whistling.

"Hello," shouted Christopher.

"Hello," said Mr Warren. "How's yourself?"

"Fine, thank you," said Christopher. "Did you put the fire out?"

"We did," said Mr Warren.

"Was it a big one?"

"It was," said Mr Warren.

"Was it a big house?" said Christopher.

"No, it was an old hay-stack," said Mr Warren. "But it was near a stable, so if we hadn't put it out the stable might have caught fire."

"Did you pump a lot of water on it?" said Christopher.

"We did and all," said Mr Warren.

"Did you go up a ladder?"

"No, we didn't need to," said Mr Warren. "Look – supposin' this apple tree was the hay-stack."

"All burning," said Christopher.

"Yes, all burning, and I stood here with one hose and . . ."

"And squirted water all over it?" said Christopher.

"Yes – and you went to the other side with another hose."

"Wait," said Christopher, "I'll go," and he ran to the other side of the apple tree and pretended he was holding a hose pipe and squirting water.

"Mine's squirting all over this side," said Christopher.

"That's right," said Mr Warren. "Well, it didn't take long to put the fire out, see?"

"No," said Christopher, "it wouldn't, would it?"

"Now, speaking of hoses," said Mr Warren, "I'm going to water those raspberry canes with your Grandma's hose this very morning."

"Oh, can I?" said Christopher. "Will you fix the hose on the tap and let me water them, then I can pretend it's a fire."

"O.K.," said Mr Warren. "And while you're doing that, I'll get on with a bit o' hedge clipping."

So Mr Warren fixed the hose on the tap at the bottom of the garden and Peter dragged the other end along the path till he got to the raspberry canes.

"Fire! Fire!" he shouted all the time. "Here comes the hose! We'll soon have it out!"

Then Mr Warren showed him how to use the hose just as if he was a fireman, and Christopher walked up and down watering the raspberry canes and pretending he was putting out a *huge* fire with the water. Wasn't he lucky?

All the time he was doing that, Mr Warren was clipping the high hedge at the bottom of the garden. One part

was so high that he had to fetch a ladder and climb up to reach the top.

At last Christopher said: "I think the fire's out now Mr Warren."

"O.K.," said Mr Warren. "Leave the hose lying there and go and turn off the water."

So Christopher did that, then he came and watched Mr Warren clipping the hedge.

"Have you ever had to climb up a ladder to put a fire out?" said Christopher.

"Yes," said Mr Warren. "Many a time. Much higher ladders than this. Yes, much higher," said Mr Warren.

"Can I climb up that ladder when you come down? And pretend I'm a fireman?" said Christopher.

"Only when I'm here," said Mr Warren.

So when he came down he showed Christopher the proper way to climb up and down a ladder, like a fireman. Christopher practised, and went up and down and up and down while Mr Warren went on clipping a lower part of the hedge. Wasn't Christopher lucky to have a real fireman to show him how to go up and down ladders properly?

At last they heard Grandmother calling.

"Ah," said Mr Warren. "Time to knock off."

So they went up the garden and sat out on a bench outside the kitchen door and Mr Warren and Grandmother had a cup of tea and talked about the things that needed doing in the garden.

And Christopher had an orange drink and thought about putting out fires with hoses and climbing very high ladders, and made up his mind that when he was a man, he'd be a fireman like Mr Warren.

blished in *Jacko and Other Stories* (Bodley Head).

The Lorry

Ruth Simonis

Once upon a time there was a man called Mr William Brown. He drove a big, heavy lorry which had a strong engine, big tyres on the wheels, and a horn that went *Too-oo-toot!*

Every morning, when the church clock struck six, every morning at that time, Mr Brown loaded up his lorry with parcels and packages and boxes and bundles and started out on a long, long drive to Birmingham. That's where he went every day – to the big town of Birmingham. And he had to drive along streets and streets and streets of houses, and shops, and factories. And every day Mr Brown said, as he drove along the streets past the houses and shops and factories: "Oh dear, I am getting tired of coming this way every day. Along the same streets, and past the same houses and shops and factories. I've come this way – every day – for twenty years, and I'm getting tired of it. Yes I *am!*"

Well, now I'll tell you what happened one morning in the summer. Mr Brown got up and made himself a cup of tea and a piece of toast. Just as the clock was striking six, he went out and loaded up his lorry with parcels and packages and boxes and bundles. And he grumbled to himself: "Oh dear, it's a nice summer morning. I don't want to go to Birmingham, along the same streets and past the same houses and shops and factories, where it's all dusty and smoky."

He got into his lorry, started it up and, with a big rumble and grumble, off they went. But when they got to the end of the road, the lorry turned to the left!

"Hi," shouted Mr William Brown, "this isn't the way to Birmingham! We should turn to the right at the end of the road for Birmingham, you know that. We've done it every morning for twenty years except on Sundays."

"We're not going to Birmingham," said the lorry. And he turned left again!

"Hi," shouted Mr William Brown, "where are we going?"

"To the seaside," said the lorry, going quicker. And he turned left again!

And before long they were out of the town and running along a small country road. There were no houses or shops or factories to be seen. Instead there were trees and flowers and grass, and birds were singing.

Then presently there were no trees; but the air was clear and shining, and soon Mr William Brown could smell a ovely clean salty smell, and then they were at the seaside.

Yes, there was the sea – big and blue and broad – tretching for miles and miles and miles. The sun was hining on it, and the little waves were jumping and parkling.

"Ah," said Mr William Brown. "This is fine," and he ook a big deep breath of the clean salty air, and stretched imself.

"Yes," said the lorry, "this is good."

"We'll have a sunbathe," said Mr William Brown. That's what we'll do."

So he drove the lorry gently down to the edge of the and, and got out, and took off his coat and cap, and rolled p his shirt-sleeves, and lay down on the beach, and had long rest in the sun. And so did the lorry. Mr Brown had is lunch with him, of course, so it was quite like a picnic.

Then they watched some children digging in the sand id making sand-castles, and some other children playing a cricket game with bats and ball. And then Mr Brown went into the water, and had a long, cool swim.

At last it was time to go. So Mr Brown got into the lorry and said: "My, that was a treat!" and the lorry said: "Too-oo-toot! It was about time we had a holiday."

Then they started back home, singing at the tops of their voices. Mr Brown drove the lorry back from the sea, through the country roads, past the trees and the grass and the flowers – back into the town, and at last he was home!

He put the lorry in the garage and said: "Good night, old friend. It's a grand day we had together."

"Yes," said the lorry, and went to sleep at once.

The Story of Pottle Pig

Nancy Northcote

Once there was a pig who lived in a comfortable sty in the corner of a farmyard. But he wasn't happy.

"It isn't fair!" he sighed. "Every Wednesday the ducks or cows ride off to market with Farmer Triggs, while I have to stay in this old farmyard all the time."

"You should think yourself lucky," said Mrs Hen as she scratched in the yard near Pottle Pig's sty. "You have a nice warm sty and plenty of good food. What more do you want?"

"I want to go to market and be sold, and go and live on another farm," answered Pottle Pig.

"You don't know when you're lucky," clucked Mrs Hen.

Next Wednesday Farmer Triggs was late in setting off for market with the ducks and cows, and in his hurry he forgot to fasten the latch on Pottle Pig's door. So after Pottle Pig had eaten his breakfast, he poked his snout out of the door and said: "It is such a nice day, I think I will walk to market by myself!" And off he trotted.

But he hadn't gone very far down the road before he began to feel hot and tired. "I wonder how far market is?" he said. "I don't want to walk much farther!"

Just then he saw a bicycle leaning against the hedge by the side of the road. "If I borrow that bicycle," he thought, "I shall soon get to market on that!" So he climbed onto the bicycle and started off down the hill.

At that moment the man who owned the bicycle came out of the field from the other side of the hedge and saw

Pottle Pig riding off. "Come back, you bad pig," he called, "that's my bicycle!"

But Pottle Pig had never ridden a bicycle before. "I can' stop!" he called out, "I don't know how to! Help! Help!"

And though the man ran as hard as he could, he couldn't catch Pottle Pig, and so the bicycle raced on down the hill, faster and faster, towards the town where the market was held.

At the bottom of the hill just outside the town was a large policeman standing in the middle of the road directi traffic, and when he saw Pottle Pig coming down the hill at such a pace he lifted his large hand in its fresh white glove right up, to tell Pottle Pig to stop. But the bicycle came bounding on and ran straight into the policeman an knocked him over flat, while Pottle Pig flew through the air and landed in the middle of a milk van, knocking the bottles clattering and smashing all over the road and making a dreadful mess!

"Young Pig," said the policeman as he picked himself
p, "you have knocked me over in the ex-e-cution of my
uty, you have splashed milk on my best uniform, there
re broken bottles all over the road, and –"

But at this moment the man who owned the bicycle
ame running down the hill calling: "Stop thief! Stop!"

"And," went on the policeman, "You did it on a stolen
icycle! You must come along with me to the police
ation and see the Sergeant."

So poor Pottle Pig was taken to the police station and
ad only bread and water for dinner that day. But the
ergeant was a kind man and soon found Farmer Triggs
ho came and took Pottle Pig back home again in his van.

And the next day, when Mrs Hen asked Pottle Pig if he
ed the market, he said: "I don't think much of markets.
hey're very dull places."

Which was naughty of him, wasn't it? For *we* know he'd
ver been to one, had he?

From the Cabbage Patch to Australia

Mary Higson

This is a story about a snail who lived in a garden of cabbages. She wanted to go to Australia – far, far away on the other side of the world.

One day the snail was very, very cross. "Bother," she said, "*bother!* Everywhere I go in this garden of cabbages I find other snails – dozens – hundreds – thousands of snails. As soon as I think I've got a cabbage to myself – along comes another snail – and another – and another. There are too many snails in the garden. Far too many, I'll go away – that's what I'll do. I'll go to Australia There will be more food there and not so many snails. I'll start at once."

So she began to slide slowly and slimily along the path that led out of the garden of cabbages.

Presently she met an earwig. "Earwig," said the snail, "is this the way to Australia?"

"Australia?" said the earwig, "Australia? Why?"

"I'm going there because there are so many snails here that I never get a cabbage to myself," said the snail.

"How right you are," said the earwig. "I think I'll com with you."

"Follow me," said the snail, and she went on sliding slov and slimily along, leaving a neat little silver path behind her so that the earwig could creep after her more easily.

Presently they met a worm. "Oh, worm," said the earwig, "is this the way to Australia?"

"Australia?" said the worm, and he looked very astonished. "Australia? Why?"

"We are going there," said the earwig, "because there are too many snails in this garden of cabbages."

"How right you are," said the worm. "I think I'll come with you."

And he went wiggle-wiggling and the earwig crept creepy-creeping along the neat little silver path the slow and sliding slimy snail made for them to follow.

Presently they met a glow-worm carrying her little lamp.

"Glow-worm," said the worm, "is this the way to Australia?"

"Australia?" said the glow-worm. "Australia? Why?"

"We are going there," said the worm, "because there are too many snails in this garden of cabbages."

"How right you are," said the glow-worm. "I think I'll come with you."

And she went crawling, crawling, and the worm went wiggly-wiggling and the earwig went creepy-creeping along the neat little silver path the slow and sliding slimy snail was making for them to follow. They went on and on and on all morning and all afternoon and all evening till at last it was quite dark.

Then the snail stopped and turned her head round and said: "Does *anybody* know where Australia is?"

"No," said the earwig, and the worm and the glow-worm.

"I'm very tired," said the snail.

"So am I," said the earwig and the worm and the glow-worm.

"I can't see a thing!" said the snail.

"Neither can I," said the earwig and the worm.

"I'll light my lamp," said the glow-worm. And she did.

"Oh-oo-oooh!" said the worm and the earwig and the snail, and they turned right round to look at the beautiful light.

"You lead the way now," said the snail, "and we will follow your light."

So the glow-worm went crawling, crawling along carrying her little lamp as high as she could.

And after her the earthworm went wiggly-wiggling and the earwig went creepy-creeping. And after her the slow and sliding slimy snail, still making a neat little silver path – although there was no one to follow her!

On and on and *on* they went, all through the long dark night, until at last it began to get light, for morning had come. Then the crawly glow-worm stopped, put out her light and looked around her.

"That's funny," she said. "This place looks exactly like the garden of cabbages we started from yesterday!"

Then the wiggly worm and the creepy earwig and the slow and sliding slimy snail looked round too, and said: "So it is!"

Then they started to laugh! And they laughed and laughed and laughed! They rolled on the ground and they laughed and laughed until they fell fast alseep. Of course, when they all turned round to follow the glow-worm's lamp they had just walked back home again!

Cherrybella's Bed

Lilian Daykin

Once upon a time there was a teeny-weeny girl called Tina. She lived in a teeny-weeny village and she was worried because she could not find a teeny-weeny bed for ier teeny-weeny dolly. She had tried all kinds of teeny-veeny beds but they were all too big, except a teeny-veeny nut shell and the teeny-weeny bed clothes fell off hat.

"Go to the teeny-weeny carpenter. He will make you a eeny-weeny bed for your teeny-weeny dolly," said her eeny-weeny mother.

So Tina went to the teeny-weeny carpenter's shop and aid: "Please, Carpenter, can you make me a teeny-weeny ed for my teeny-weeny dolly?"

"Let me see your teeny-weeny dolly," said the teeny-veeny carpenter. "I must measure her to find out the size make her a teeny-weeny bed."

So Tina opened her hand, and there lay the teeny-weeny oll, not much bigger than the teeny-weeny nail on Tina's eny-weeny hand.

"Oh, my goodness me!" said the teeny-weeny carpenter. No wonder you lose her! What do you call her?"

"Cherrybella," said Tina, "don't you think it is a lovely ame?"

"Oh yes, I do," answered the teeny-weeny carpenter. But isn't it a rather big name for such a teeny-weeny eature? Why, she's not as big as a teeny-weeny asshopper!"

"Now you have seen her," said Tina, "you know how

easily she can get lost. Can you make her a teeny-weeny bed? I don't know what I should do if she got lost altogether."

"That surely would be a pity," said the teeny-weeny carpenter. "She is the daintiest, teeny-weeny dollie I have ever seen. But I am afraid I cannot help you, for even if I could measure her with my teeny-weeny rule, I have no teeny-weeny saw fine enough to saw the wood to make her bed teeny-weeny enough."

"Oh dear!" said Tina. "I do wish I had a teeny-weeny bed for Cherrybella. I am so afraid I will lose her."

"Why not try the teeny-weeny shoemaker?" suggested the teeny-weeny carpenter. "He might stitch you one of leather."

So Tina went to the teeny-weeny shoemaker. She could hear him tapping on his teeny-weeny last as she opened the teeny-weeny door.

"Please, teeny-weeny Shoemaker," said Tina, "can you make a teeny-weeny dollie a teeny-weeny bed to keep her warm and safe at night?"

The teeny-weeny shoemaker looked at her over the top of his teeny-weeny spectacles. "I have made most things in my time, my dear teeny-weeny child, so no doubt I could make you a teeny-weeny bed for your teeny-weeny dollie. Of course I shall have to measure her, everything I sell is made to measure, you know."

"That's what I am afraid of," said Tina, "for the teeny-weeny carpenter said he might not be able to measure her with his teeny-weeny ruler and he had no teeny-weeny saw fine enough to make her bed teeny-weeny enough."

"Show me the teeny-weeny dollie and no doubt I will be able to make her a teeny-weeny bed," said the teeny-weeny shoemaker. "For my work is far finer than any the teeny-weeny carpenter can do."

Then Tina opened her teeny-weeny hand and showed him Cherrybella, and said: "Here she is."

"Where?" asked the teeny-weeny shoemaker. "I can see no teeny-weeny dollie." Then he bent down lower and looked through his teeny-weeny spectacles instead of over them, and he could just see Cherrybella lying on Tina's teeny-weeny pink hand.

"Oh, my goodness me!" he exclaimed. "Mm – you've set me a task this time and no mistake. I don't think I could see to stitch the teeny-weeny stitches that would be needed to make such a teeny-weeny bed for your Cherrybella."

"I shall lose Cherrybella if I don't find her a teeny-weeny bed," said Tina, and a teeny-weeny tear trickled down her teeny-weeny nose. "I know I shall lose her."

"Dry your teeny-weeny eyes, Tina," said the

teeny-weeny shoemaker, for he was the kindest of teeny-weeny men and had teeny-weeny grandchildren of his own. "Go along to the teeny-weeny watchmaker. He has the finest teeny-weeny tools in teeny-weeny village, and the strongest teeny-weeny spectacles. He will make you a teeny-weeny bed for your teeny-weeny dolly if anyone can."

So Tina went to the teeny-weeny watchmaker's shop. "Do you think that you could make a teeny-weeny bed for the tiniest dolly in all the teeny-weeny world?" asked Tina.

The teeny-weeny old man looked at her kindly but waited until all the teeny-weeny clocks in his teeny-weeny shop had finished striking four o'clock before he replied: "I am sure that I can make you a teeny-weeny bed for your teeny-weeny dolly," said the watchmaker, "no matter how teeny-weeny she may be." And he sounded so certain that Tina began to feel happy at once. Then she opened her

teeny-weeny hand and showed him teeny-weeny Cherrybella.

"Well," he said, "I must say that I have *never* in all my long life seen such a teeny-weeny dolly, but I will see what I can do."

Then out of a teeny-weeny drawer he took a teeny-weeny box with teeny-weeny coloured flowers painted on the lid. "Now what have we here?" he said, opening the teeny-weeny lid.

Inside there was a teeny-weeny red velvet mattress and a teeny-weeny white satin pillow. "There," said the teeny-weeny watchmaker, "see if that will fit your teeny-weeny treasure."

Tina laid Cherrybella in the teeny-weeny box and the teeny-weeny watchmaker covered her with a teeny-weeny quilt of cotton wool. "Now your teeny-weeny dolly has a teeny-weeny bed. If you want to carry her in your teeny-weeny pocket the teeny-weeny lid will keep her safe." And – click! he shut the teeny-weeny lid.

"Oh thank you!" said Tina. "That is the loveliest bed my darling Cherrybella could have. How much is it, please?"

"It is a present," said the teeny-weeny watchmaker, "a present for the teeny-weeniest doll I have ever seen in all my long life."

"Oh thank you!" said Tina again, and she gave the kind old watchmaker a teeny-tiny kiss. Then she ran back along the teeny-weeny lane to her teeny-weeny home.

Published in *Ten Minutes to Bedtime* (George G. Harrap).

Dan Pig

Peggy Worvill

Dan Pig lived in a pig-sty at the end of the garden. The pig-sty had two rooms – an outside room and an inside room. The outside room had a trough in one corner for Dan Pig to eat his dinner out of; and a piece of wood in the other corner for Dan Pig to scratch his back against. The inside room had a big heap of clean straw in it for Dan Pig to sleep on. Near the sty grew an apple tree to make cool shade for Dan Pig in the summer. One hot sunny day, Dan Pig stood in his outside room and waited for something to happen.

By and by a dog came along the garden path. Dan Pig stood very still and quiet. The dog put his nose under the door of the sty.

"Hunc," said Dan Pig.

The dog was so startled he ran away into his kennel as fast as he could, and stayed there for a long time.

That *did* make Dan Pig laugh. "Hunc, hunc, hunc," he went. "Hunc, hunc, hunc!"

Then he stood still in his outside room and waited for something else to happen.

By and by a cat came along the garden path. Dan Pig stood very still and quiet. The cat put her nose under the door of the sty.

"Hunc!" said Dan Pig.

The cat was so startled she ran away as fast as she could, right up to the top of the apple tree, and stayed there for a long time.

That *did* make Dan Pig laugh. "Hunc, hunc, hunc," he went. "Hunc, hunc, hunc!"

Then he stood very still in his outside room and waited for something else to happen.

By and by Missis came along the path. She carried Dan Pig's dinner in a bucket. Dan Pig stood very still and quiet. Missis opened the door of the sty.

"Hunc!" said Dan Pig, then he took the corner of Missis's apron into his mouth and pulled it.

"All right, Dan Pig," said Missis, "now leave my apron alone and have your dinner," and she tried to pull the apron out of Dan Pig's mouth. Dan Pig pulled hard, and Missis pulled hard. But Dan Pig pulled harder, and suddenly Missis's apron came right off and fell on the floor of the sty.

That *did* make Dan Pig laugh. "Hunc, hunc, hunc," he went. "Hunc, hunc, hunc!"

"There now, look what you've done," said Missis crossly. "Whatever has come over you today?"

Then Dan Pig saw that the door of the pig-sty was open, so he ran right out!

"Come back at once, Dan Pig!" called Missis, and she began to run after him.

But Dan Pig knew she couldn't catch him, and he ran all round the garden three times before he went back into the sty. Missis ran in after him, all out of breath, and shut the door – bang.

"There," she said, "now you just eat up your dinner, Dan Pig." And she filled up his trough with a nice dinner of potatoes and gravy.

"I don't want this dinner," said Dan Pig. "I don't want potatoes and gravy. I want nice juicy green grass." And he put his nose into the trough and began to push his dinner about. He pushed it out of the trough and all over the floor of the sty.

That *did* make Dan Pig laugh! "Hunc, hunc, hunc," he went. "Hunc, hunc, hunc!"

Then Dan Pig lay down and rolled over and over. When he stood up, there were pieces of potato all over his back and on his head, and in his ears, and gravy was running down his nose.

"Dan Pig, Dan Pig, I'm surprised at you!" said Missis, "I don't know what's come over you today." And she picked up the bucket and went away and shut the door of her house – bang!

When she was gone, Dan Pig felt very uncomfortable. A piece of potato fell into his eye. Gravy was tickling his nose. He felt so hot.

By and by he heard Missis coming back along the path. Dan Pig stood very still and quiet; Missis opened the door of the sty but he didn't say a word! Missis was carrying a bucket of water and a big scrubbing brush like the one she used to scrub the kitchen floor. "Now you stand still, Dan

Pig," said Missis. "I've never seen such a dirty pig in all my life." She dipped her brush into the water and began to scrub Dan Pig's back. Dan Pig stood very still. Missis scrubbed away all the dinner from Dan Pig's back, and head and nose. And then she lifted up his ears and scrubbed round those. Dan Pig liked that. When he was clean again, Missis threw a bucket of water all over him and said: "Now shake yourself." And Dan Pig did. Then she got more water and a long broom and she washed and brushed the floor of the sty till it was clean again. Then she went away, and Dan Pig stood drying in the sun.

By and by Missis came back. Her apron was full of nice juicy green grass. She put it into Dan Pig's trough and he ate up every bit. He had just finished when a little green apple fell off the apple tree. It fell right into Dan Pig's trough!

That *did* make Dan Pig laugh! "Hunc, hunc, hunc," he went. "Hunc, hunc, hunc!" And he ate that little sour green apple up too, stalk and skin, and pips and all.

Then he went into his inside room. He lay down on his heap of straw and fell fast asleep, snoring.

Going Fishing

Dorothy Edwards

One day, when I was a little girl, and my sister was a very little girl, some children came to our house and asked my mother if I could go fishing with them.

They were carrying jam-jars with string tied round the top, and they had fishing-nets over their shoulders. They had paper bags with sandwiches in them and they had a bottle of lemonade each. So my mother said: "Yes, you can go fishing with the children," and she found *me* a jam-jar and a fishing-net, and she cut *me* some sandwiches.

Then my naughty little sister said: "I want to go fishing, I want to go fishing. I want to go fishing too!" just like that.

So my mother said, "Well, you'd better take her too."

Then my mother cut some sandwiches for my little sister, but she didn't give her a jam-jar or a fishing-net because she said she was too little to go near the water. She gave her a basket to put stones in instead, because my little sister liked to pick up stones, and she gave me a *big* bottle of lemonade to carry for both of us.

My mother said: "You mustn't let your little sister get herself wet. You must keep her away from the water."

And I said: "All right, Mother, I promise."

So then we all went off to the little river, and we took our shoes and socks off, and we tucked up our clothes, and we walked into the water to catch fish with our fishing-nets, and we filled our jam-jars with water to put the fishes in when we caught them. And we said to my naughty little sister, "You mustn't come into the water. You'll get yourself wet. You stay and pick up stones on the bank."

Then we others paddled and paddled and fished and fished, but we didn't catch any fish at all, not even one little tiny one. Then one of the boys said to me, "Look, there is your little sister – *she's* in the water too!"

And, do you know, my naughty little sister had walked right into the water with her shoes and socks on, and she was trying to catch fish in her little basket.

I said: "Get out of the water," and she said, "No."

I said: "Get out *at once*," and she said, "I don't care." Wasn't she naughty?

So I said: "I must fetch you out then," and my naughty little sister tried to run away in the water, and she fell down and she got wet all over.

She got her frock wet, and her petticoat wet, and her knickers wet, and her vest wet, and her hat wet, and her hair-ribbon all soaking wet.

And she cried and cried.

So we fetched her out of the water, and we said: "Oh dear, she will catch a cold," and we took off her wet hat, and her wet frock, and her wet petticoat, and her wet knickers, and her wet vest, and her wet hair-ribbon, *and* her wet shoes and socks, and we hung them all to dry on the bushes in the sunshine. And we wrapped my naughty little sister up in my woolly cardigan. But still my little sister cried and cried. So we gave her the sandwiches and she ate them all up.

She ate her sandwiches and my sandwiches and the other children's sandwiches all up. And still she cried and cried.

Then one of the children gave her an apple, and another of the children gave her some toffees, and while she was eating those, we took her clothes off the bushes and ran about flapping them in the sunshine until they were quite dry.

When her clothes were quite dry, we put them all back on her again, and she cried and cried because she didn't want her clothes on any more.

So I took her home, and then she stopped crying, and my mother said: "Oh, you've let your little sister fall into the water."

And I said: "How do you know, because we dried all her clothes?"

And my mother said: "Yes, but you couldn't iron them; they're all crumpled up and messy."

Then my mother said my little sister must go straight to bed, and have some hot milk. And my mother said to my little sister: "Don't you think you were a naughty little girl to go in the water?"

And my naughty little sister said: "I won't do it any more, because it was too wet."

But, do you know, when my mother went to throw away the stones out of my sister's basket, she found a little fish in the bottom which my naughty little sister had caught!

Published in *My Naughty Little Sister* (Methuen).

Butch Goes to Market
Celia Felgate

Once upon a time there was a handsome brown-and-white dog whose name was Butch. He lived in a cottage about a mile along the lane that led into the town.

One morning when he woke up he saw the sun shining through his bedroom window and the sky was blue, and he thought to himself: "I think I will go to the market today and see what I can buy." So up he got and off he went.

He had only got as far as the front gate when he saw Pussy Cat sitting in the middle of the path.

"Good morning, Pussy Cat," said Butch.

"Good morning, Butch," said Pussy Cat. "Where are you off to today?"

"Well, it's *such* a nice morning this morning that I thought to myself, 'I think I'll go to the market and see what I can buy'."

"Miaow," said Pussy Cat, "can I come too?"

"Woof, woof," said Butch. "Of course you can. Come along."

And off they went together – left, right, left, right.

They hadn't gone very far along the lane when they came across Mr Piggy, sitting in the middle of the road.

"Good morning, Mr Piggy," said Butch.

"Good morning, Butch," said Mr Piggy. "Where are you off to today?"

"Well, it was *such* a nice morning this morning that I thought to myself, 'I think I'll go to the market and see what I can buy'. And on the way I met Pussy Cat and he wanted to come too, so we are both off together."

"Grunt, grunt," said Mr Piggy. "Can I come too?"

"Woof, woof," said Butch. "Of course you can. Come along."

And off they all went together – left, right, left, right.

They hadn't gone very far along the lane when they came across Little Lamb sitting in the middle of the road.

"Good morning, Little Lamb," said Butch.

"Good morning, Butch," said Little Lamb. "Where are you off to today?"

"Well, it was *such* a nice morning this morning that I thought to myself, 'I think I will go to the market and see what I can buy'. And on the way I met Pussy Cat and Mr Piggy and they wanted to come too, so we are all off together."

"Baa, baa," said Little Lamb. "Can I come too?"

"Woof, woof," said Butch. "Of course you can. Come along."

And off they all went together – left, right, left, right.

They hadn't gone very far along the lane when they came across Mrs Hen and her little chicks, sitting in the middle of the road.

"Good morning, Mrs Hen," said Butch.

"Good morning, Butch," said Mrs Hen. "Where are ou off to today?"

"Well, it was *such* a nice morning this morning that I hought to myself, 'I think I'll go to the market and see vhat I can buy'. And on the way I met Pussy Cat and Mr ig and Little Lamb and they all wanted to come too, so ve are all off together."

"Coo-oop, coo-oop," said Mrs Hen. "Can I and my ttle chicks come too?"

"Woof, woof," said Butch. "Of course you can. Come long."

And off they all went together – left, right, left, right.

They hadn't gone very far along the lane when they came across two little Ducks, sitting in the middle of the road.

"Good morning, little Ducks," said Butch.

"Good morning, Butch," said the little Ducks. "Where are you off to today!"

"Well, it was *such* a nice morning this morning that I thought to myself, 'I think I will go to the market and see what I can buy'. And on the way I met Pussy Cat and Mr Piggy and Little Lamb and Mrs Hen and her little chicks and they all wanted to come too, so we are all off together."

"Quack-quack, quack-quack," said the little Ducks. "Can we come too?"

"Woof, woof," said Butch. "Of course you can."

And off they all went together – left, right, left, right.

But it seemed such a long way to the market and the day was so hot that they walked more slowly – left, right, left, right – and more slowly still – until . . . what do you think they heard?

"Brrm, brrm, beep, beep," and round the corner

came Old Motor Car, and he stopped, all puffing and panting, beside them.

"Good morning, Butch," said Old Motor Car. "Where are you off to today?"

"Good morning, Old Motor Car." said Butch. "Well, it was *such* a nice morning this morning that I thought to myself, 'I think I will go to the market and see what I can buy'. And on the way I met Pussy Cat and Mr Piggy and Little Lamb and Mrs Hen and her little chicks and two little Ducks and they *all* wanted to come too, so we are all off together – but, oh dear, it is so hot and we are all so tired."

"Brrm, brrm," said Old Motor Car. "Well, all hop in and I will take you to the market because I would like to go too!"

So in they all got and away they went . . . "Brrm, brrm, beep, beep," and what a lovely day they had! They all enjoyed themselves so much that they often meet together now and go to the market in Old Motor Car and you can hear them going along the lane like this . . . "Brrm, brrm, beep, beep!"

The Tiny Little Rabbit

Ruth Borchard

Once upon a time there was a tiny little rabbit.
The tiny little rabbit jumped about: up and down in the grass, and up and hop over the path, and up and hop over the flowers, and up and *hopla* hop even over the Mummy rabbit!

"That was a fine big jump, tiny little rabbit," said the Mummy rabbit. "But now it is time to go to bed."

"No – no – no," cried the tiny little rabbit. "I don't want to go to sleep."

"Yes, it is late, and you are tired, and now you go to bed," said the Mummy rabbit.

"No, I am not tired, and I don't want to go to sleep," said the tiny little rabbit.

So when the Mummy rabbit had put the tiny little rabbit to bed, the tiny little rabbit kept its eyes open, and stayed awake for a long time.

It grew quite dark and very late. It grew so late that Mummy rabbit came to bed, too. And still the tiny little rabbit was awake.

Then the tiny little rabbit got up and went out. Outside it was so dark, and it was so quiet. There were the birds, all fast asleep on the trees, there was the tiny little dog – fast asleep, there was the tiny little kitten – fast asleep, there was the tiny little chicken – fast asleep, there was the tiny little fish – fast asleep, there were all the little boys and girls and their mummies and daddies – all fast asleep.

Only the tiny little rabbit would not go to sleep.

The tiny little rabbit hopped about very quietly. Did nobody want to play? No, everybody was fast asleep. Even the grass was lying down flat and the flowers had closed their eyes.

And the tiny little rabbit was all alone in the dark and it was cold.

Quick – quick – quick the tiny little rabbit hopped into its bed.

Quick – quick – quick, it closed its eyes.

And quick – quick – quick, it fell fast asleep in its cosy little bed.

Sleep tight, tiny little rabbit.

The Tiny Little Chicken

Ruth Borchard

Here is a story about a little chicken. It's a very tiny little chicken, just like a soft round ball of yellow fluff, and it runs about calling: "Peep, peep, peep," like that. "Peep, peep, peep."

Once upon a time this tiny little chick was running about in the garden gaily and happily.

And there was a Mummy hen making scratch, scratch, scratch on the ground for some food for the tiny little chick.

"Glook, glook, glook, tiny little chick," said the Mummy hen. "Don't go out of the gate, you may get lost."

But one day, when the gate was left open, out ran the tiny little chick, out of the garden, into the big street.

First the tiny chick ran – ran – ran, looking round – round – round.

Then it wanted something to eat. And the tiny little chick ran – ran – ran, looking round – round – round, but there was NO Mummy hen, and the tiny little chick was VERY FRIGHTENED.

But then the tiny little chick saw the open gate, and heard the Mummy calling, "Glook, glook, glook, here's some food on the ground for my chick, chick, chick. Come along to your Mummy, tiny little chick, chick, chick."

And the tiny little chick RAN through the open gate, back to the Mummy hen gaily and happily crying: "Peep, peep, peep."

Crackers the Christmas Cat

Ursula Hourihane

Once upon a time there was a small white cat. He lived in a big old house called Number Four in a street in London. He had nice children to play with and plenty of toys, a cosy fire to sleep by, and lots of good things to eat and drink. So you can see he was a very lucky little cat.

One day, just before Christmas, Crackers was lying on the rug in front of the fire thinking. Suddenly he had a grand idea!

"I know what I'll do, *I'll* give presents to all *my* friends this Christmas – I'll be a Father Christmas CAT!" And he was so excited and pleased that he started to chase his short white tail round and round in circles till he was quite dizzy, and had to sit down! "First I must find some nice presents," he thought. So he scampered over to the children's toy cupboard and began to poke about.

"Oh," he said, "here's a little rubber ball. That will do for Stumpy the cat at Number Five," and he hid it behind a cushion in the armchair. "And this small rag book with pictures of animals will do for Moppet at Number Nine," he said, and he hid that. "This old doll's hat with a blue feather will do for Mrs Tibs at Number Seven," and he hid it behind the cushion too.

After that he found a little woolly ball, a doll's bead necklace, an old Christmas card with a picture of a robin, and a bright blue golliwog made of darning wool.

"That should be enough," said Crackers. "Now I must find a sack to carry them in." He scampered downstairs to the place where the children's shoe-bags were hanging, and chose one with gay flowers on it. He had to climb very carefully along the back of a chair to get near enough to unhook the bag off its peg; then darted upstairs again and hid it behind the cushion too.

"Now," said Crackers, "I can't do anything else till tonight."

It seemed a very long time till the children were in bed. But at last there was no one about and Crackers began to pack his sack with the presents for his cat friends.

The children had tied a new red ribbon round his neck to make him look gay for Christmas, and had hung a tiny silver bell under his chin so that he made a tinkle-tinkle noise when he moved.

"I hope no one will hear me," he said to himself. "But p'raps people will just think it's Christmas bells ringing." His sack was full now, so he held the string tightly in his sharp little teeth and jumped up on to the window-sill. *Tinkle! Tinkle!* Oh dear! Crackers thought everyone in the house must have heard the little bell. But no one came. He looked out of the window. Everything was very still. A big round moon was making the snow shine and sparkle like silver.

"It looks very pretty," said Crackers, "but very cold."

The window was open at the top and Crackers had to give a huge jump to reach the ledge. *Tinkle! Tinkle!* Crackers thought everyone in the world must have heard the little silver bell. This time it sounded so loud in the quiet air. But nobody came.

Crackers climbed up onto the roof quite easily and began to walk very carefully over the snowy roof-tops. His soft feet didn't make a sound and his coat was so white

that you couldn't have seen him against the snow. Every now and then his little silver bell rang.

When he came to the chimney of Number Nine, Crackers said: "I don't think I'd better go down the chimneys like that Father Christmas man. I'm not magic like him. *I* should get all sooty and dirty. I'll just drop my presents down the chimneys. That should be all right." So he dropped the rag book down the chimney. "That will be a nice surprise for Moppet in the morning."

It took a long time to drop the presents down the chimneys and Crackers was beginning to feel rather tired when he came to Number Twenty-one – the last of all. He was just going to drop the bead necklace down the chimney when he heard a far-away jingle-jingle sound. "That's not my bell," said Crackers.

He listened again. Now the bells were nearer and louder. Who could be coming at this time of night when everyon was in bed and asleep?

And then over the snowy roof-tops came – who do you

hink? Why, Father Christmas himself, with his galloping
eindeer and silver sleigh.

"Hello! Hello!" called Father Christmas, cheerily.
'Who's this I see?" and he hopped out of his sleigh.

"Bless me, if it isn't Crackers – the little Father
Christmas Cat. Well! Well! isn't that grand?" And he
tooped down and picked up Crackers in his warm hands
nd stroked his soft white coat. Then he saw the pretty
ead necklace in Crackers' paw. "Oho!" he cried. "What's
his?"

"It's a present for Belinda Tabbycat," said Crackers.

"I'll pop down the chimney with it," said Father
Christmas, "and then I'll take you for a ride over the
oof-tops for a Christmas treat."

Father Christmas went down the chimney as fast as
ghtning and, sure enough, when he came up again, his
d coat was just as fresh and clean as ever! He put
rackers into the sleigh beside him and off they went –
ngling and tinkling over the snowy roof-tops.

The next thing Crackers knew . . . he was waking up in the armchair in front of the fire in his own cosy home again at Number Four. But Crackers knew he hadn't been dreaming, for the empty shoe-bag was there on the floor beside the chair. And there – on the cushion near his head, was a pink sugar mouse. A label was tied round its neck, saying: A PRESENT FROM FATHER CHRISTMAS!